PRENTICE HALL
Chemistry

Guided Reading
and
Study Workbook

TEACHER'S EDITION

PEARSON

Prentice
Hall

Needham, Massachusetts
Upper Saddle River, New Jersey

Cover photograph: Image from Getty Images, Inc.

ISBN 0-13-190415-9

1 2 3 4 5 6 7 8 9 10   08 07 06 05 04

CONTENTS

INTRODUCTION TO CHEMISTRY

SECTION 1.1 CHEMISTRY (pages 7–11)

This section defines chemistry and differentiates among its traditional divisions. It also distinguishes pure from applied chemistry and provides several reasons to study chemistry.

▶ What Is Chemistry? (page 7)

1. What is matter?

   Matter is anything that has mass and takes up space.

2. What is chemistry?

   Chemistry is the study of the composition of matter and the changes that

   matter undergoes.

▶ Areas of Study (page 8)

3. What are the five major areas of chemistry?

   a. organic chemistry

   b. inorganic chemistry

   c. analytical chemistry

   d. physical chemistry

   e. biochemistry

4. Is the following sentence true or false? The boundaries between the five areas of chemistry are not firm. _____true_____

5. Complete the table by filling in the appropriate subdivision of chemistry.

physical chemistry	Investigating ways to slow down the rusting of steel
biochemistry	Developing a better insulin-delivery system for diabetics
analytical chemistry	Determining the amount of mercury present in a soil sample
inorganic chemistry	Comparing the hardness of copper and silver
organic chemistry	Developing a new carbon-based fiber for clothing

CHAPTER 1, Introduction to Chemistry *(continued)*

▶ Pure and Applied Chemistry (page 9)

6. _____Applied_____ chemistry is research that is directed toward a
practical goal or application; _____pure_____ chemistry is the
pursuit of chemical knowledge for its own sake.

▶ Why Study Chemistry? (pages 10–11)

7. Why is the study of chemistry important?

   a. _explaining the natural world_____

   b. _preparing for a career_____

   c. _being an informed citizen_____

8. List three careers that require some knowledge of chemistry.

   _firefighter, turf manager, and photographer_____

📖 Reading Skill Practice

Outlining can help you understand and remember what you have read. Write an outline for Section 1.1, Chemistry. Begin your outline by copying the headings in the textbook. Under each heading, write the main idea. Then list the details that support the main idea. Do your work on a separate sheet of paper.

Students' outlines should have four major topics, matching the four headings of the section. Details should include all the highlighted key terms, as well as the important concepts discussed under each heading.

SECTION 1.2 CHEMISTRY FAR AND WIDE (pages 12–17)

This section summarizes ways in which chemistry affects many aspects of life.

▶ Materials (page 12)

1. Is the following statement true or false? Chemists design materials to fit general
   needs. _____false_____

2. In George de Mestral's hook-and-loop tapes, were the hooks macroscopic or
   microscopic? _____microscopic_____

▶ Energy (page 13)

3. List two ways to meet the demand for energy.

   a. _____conserving energy_____

   b. _____producing more energy_____

4. How does insulation help conserve energy?

   Insulation acts as a barrier to heat flow.

5. How are soybeans used as a source of energy?

   Soybean plants can be used to make biodiesel, a fuel that burns more cleanly

   than regular diesel.

6. Circle the letter of the statement that is always true about a battery.

   a. All batteries are able to be recharged.

   b. Batteries use chemicals to store energy.

   c. Batteries are devices that conserve energy.

   d. NASA developed batteries that are thrown away after use.

▶ Medicine and Biotechnology (page 14)

7. What is the role of chemistry in the development of medicines?

   Chemists use knowledge of the structure and function of chemicals in cells to design

   safe and effective drugs.

8. List three new materials chemists have developed that have medical applications.

   a. plastic tubes to replace diseased arteries

   b. artificial hips and knees

   c. plastic "skin" that can heal itself when it cracks

9. The field that applies science to the production of biological products is

   _____biotechnology_____ .

CHAPTER 1, Introduction to Chemistry *(continued)*

10. Complete the concept map about genes.

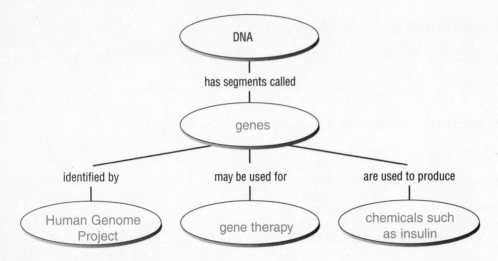

▶ Agriculture (page 15)

11. How do chemists contribute to agriculture?

Chemists help to develop more productive crops and safer, more effective ways to

protect crops.

_____

12. How can a potato plant modified with a jellyfish gene help a farmer to conserve water?

The modified potato plant glows when it needs water.

_____

_____

13. What type of pesticides do chemists design to protect crops?

Chemists design pesticides that only kill specific insects because some insects are

helpful and shouldn't be destroyed.

14. In Figure 1.11, how does the plastic tube around the tomato stem protect the plant?

The plastic tube emits a chemical that attracts male pinworm moths, which reduces

the number of harmful pinworms produced.

_____

▶ The Environment (page 16)

15. What are two ways that chemists work to protect the environment?

　　a. identify pollutants _____

　　b. prevent pollution _____

16. Define a pollutant.

A pollutant is a material found in air, water, and soil that is harmful to humans or

other organisms.

17. How is lead harmful to humans?

Low levels of lead in the blood can permanently damage the nervous system,

especially of growing children.

18. What strategies have been used to prevent lead poisoning in children?

blood testing; regulating sales of older homes to families with younger children;

public awareness campaigns

▶ The Universe (page 17)

19. Scientists can learn about the chemical composition of stars by analyzing

the _____ light _____ they transmit.

20. Why won't the method used to discover the chemical composition of stars
work for the moon and planets?

The moon and planets do not emit light.

21. What did chemists learn about the moon's surface by analyzing moon rocks?

They learned that oceans of lava once covered the moon's surface.

22. Look at Figure 1.14 on page 17. What is the key difference in the methods
scientists used to analyze rocks from Earth's moon and Mars?

Astronauts collected rock samples from Earth's moon.

Rocks on Mars were analyzed by a robotic vehicle.

CHAPTER 1, Introduction to Chemistry *(continued)*

SECTION 1.3 THINKING LIKE A SCIENTIST (pages 20–25)

This section describes the development of an experimental approach to chemistry and steps involved in the scientific method. It also discusses the role of collaboration and communication in science.

▶ Alchemy (page 20)

1. Practical alchemy focused on

   developing techniques for working with metals, glass, and dyes.

   _____

2. Alchemists developed processes for separating ____mixtures____ and

   purifying ____chemicals____.

▶ An Experimental Approach to Science (page 21)

3. How did Lavoisier help to transform chemistry?

   He demonstrated the importance of measurement.

   _____

4. Circle the letter of the word that identifies what Lavoisier demonstrated was necessary for materials to burn.

   a. phlogiston

   b. nitrogen

   c. oxygen

   d. metals

▶ The Scientific Method (pages 22–23)

5. What is the scientific method?

   It is a logical systematic, approach to the solution of a scientific problem.

   _____

6. Complete the flowchart about the scientific method.

A scientific problem is often discovered when an _____observation_____ is made, which leads to a question.

↓

A _____hypothesis_____ is formed when an explanation is proposed for an observation.

↓

Testing a proposed explanation requires designing an _____experiment_____ .

↓

For the results of the test to be accepted, the test must produce the same results _____when repeated_____ .

↓

An explanation may become a _____theory_____ if the same results are found after many tests.

7. Circle the letter of the activity that involves using the senses to gather information directly.

a. forming a hypothesis

b. making an observation

c. planning an experiment

d. analyzing data

8. What do scientists do if the results of an experiment do not support the hypothesis?

They develop a new hypothesis and perform experiments to test the new hypothesis.

_____

9. The variable that you change during an experiment is the _____manipulated variable_____ .

The variable that is observed during an experiment is the _____responding variable_____ .

CHAPTER 1, Introduction to Chemistry *(continued)*

10. Is the following sentence true or false? Once a theory has been proven, no experiment will ever disprove it. _____false_____

11. What is a scientific law?

A scientific law is a concise statement that summarizes the results of many

observations and experiments.

12. Circle the letter of each statement that expresses a scientific law.

    a. As the temperature of a balloon increases, the balloon expands.

    b. Increasing the temperature of a balloon might cause it to burst.

    (c.) If all other variables are kept constant, the volume of a gas increases as the temperature increases.

    d. Sometimes increasing the temperature of a gas causes the gas to expand.

▶ Collaboration and Communication (pages 24–25)

13. Several scientists working together to solve a problem is _____collaboration_____.

14. Is the following statement true or false? Scientists from different disciplines may need to work together on a problem because the problem is too complex for one person to solve. _____true_____

15. Exchanging ideas about science is called _____communication_____ .

16. How are journals helpful to scientists?

Scientists use journals to keep up with new discoveries.

17. Is the following statement true or false? Experts in an author's field review articles after they are published in a journal. _____false_____ .

SECTION 1.4 PROBLEM SOLVING IN CHEMISTRY (pages 28–32)

This section describes effective approaches for solving numeric problems and conceptual problems.

▶ Skills Used in Solving Problems (page 28)

1. Name an everyday situation that requires problem-solving skills.

   Students' answers will vary, but should include aspects of problem solving.

2. What is involved in effective problem solving?

   developing a plan and implementing that plan

▶ Solving Numeric Problems (pages 29–30)

3. What are the three steps for solving numeric problems?

   a. _____analyze_____

   b. _____calculate_____

   c. _____evaluate_____

4. What must you determine first when solving a word problem?

   where you are starting from (what is known) and where you are going (the unknown)

5. What are two skills that you may need to use as you calculate an answer to a problem?

   converting a measurement from one unit to another and rearranging an equation

   to solve for an unknown

6. If your answer to a problem does not seem reasonable, list two things you can do.

   Possible answers: Reread the problem. Make an estimate of the answer.

CHAPTER 1, Introduction to Chemistry *(continued)*

7. For the following word problem, fill in the table, listing the known and unknown information: A person can walk a mile in 20 minutes. The person is going for a 10-mile walk. How many hours will it take for the person to complete the walk?

Known	Unknown
total distance = 10 miles	total time = ? h
rate of walking = 1 mile in 20 minutes	
number of minutes in an hour = 60	

▶ Solving Conceptual Problems (pages 31–32)

8. After you identify the known and unknown in a conceptual problem, what should you do next?

Make a plan for getting from the unknown to the known.

9. What are the steps for solving conceptual problems?

analyze and solve

2 MATTER AND CHANGE

SECTION 2.1 PROPERTIES OF MATTER (pages 39–42)

This section helps you distinguish extensive from intensive properties and identify substances by their properties. It teaches you how to differentiate the three states of matter. It also defines a physical property and lists examples of physical properties and physical changes.

▶ **Describing Matter** (page 39)

1. The _____ mass _____ of an object is a measure of the amount of matter the object contains.

2. How does an extensive property differ from an intensive property?

   An extensive property depends on the amount of matter, while an intensive property
   _____
   depends on the type of matter.
   _____

▶ **Identifying Substances** (page 40)

3. Matter that has a uniform and definite composition is called a
   _____ substance _____ .

4. Is the following sentence true or false? All samples of a substance have different physical properties. _____ false _____

5. A physical property is a quality or condition of a substance that can be
   _____ observed _____ or _____ measured _____ without changing the substance's composition.

6. Circle the letter of the term that is NOT a physical property.

   a. hardness   **c.** boiling point

   b. color   **d.** melting   ⟵ (circled)

7. Look at Table 2.1 on page 40. What is the melting point of bromine? −7°C

8. Look at Table 2.1 on page 40. Circle the letter of the substance that is a yellow solid and melts at 115°C.

   a. sulfur   ⟵ (circled)

   b. chlorine

   c. gold

   d. copper

CHAPTER 2, Matter and Change *(continued)*

9. Is the following sentence true or false? Physical properties can help a chemist identify a substance. _____ true _____

▶ **States of Matter** (pages 41–42)

10. Circle the letter of the term that is NOT a physical state of matter.

(a.) water

b. gas

c. liquid

d. solid

11. Complete the table about properties of three states of matter. Use these terms: *definite, indefinite, easily,* and *not easily.*

Properties of the States of Matter			
Property	**Solid**	**Liquid**	**Gas or Vapor**
Shape	definite	indefinite	indefinite
Volume	definite	definite	indefinite
Can be compressed	not easily	not easily	easily

12. Match each arrangement of the particles in matter with a physical state.

Physical State	Arrangement
__c__ gas	**a.** packed tightly together
__b__ liquid	**b.** close, but free to flow
__a__ solid	**c.** spaced relatively far apart

13. Is the following sentence true or false? The words *gas* and *vapor* can be used interchangeably. _____ false _____

14. The term gas is limited to those substances that exist in the gaseous state at _____ room temperature _____ .

15. What does *vapor* describe?

Vapor describes the gaseous state of a substance that is generally a liquid or solid

at room temperature.

▶ Physical Changes (page 42)

16. A physical change alters a given material without changing its chemical
_____composition_____ .

17. What are some words that describe physical changes?

boil, freeze, dissolve, melt, condense, break, split, crack, grind, cut, and crush

18. What is true about all physical changes that involve a change of state?

They are all reversible.

SECTION 2.2 MIXTURES (pages 44–47)

This section explains how to classify a mixture as heterogeneous or homogeneous. It also describes ways to separate mixtures.

▶ Classifying Mixtures (pages 44–45)

1. Is the following sentence true or false? Most samples of matter are mixtures.
_____true_____

2. What is a mixture?

A mixture is a physical blend of two or more components.

3. Is the following sentence true or false? A heterogeneous mixture is one that
has a completely uniform composition. _____false_____

4. What is another name for a homogeneous mixture?
_____a solution_____

5. Circle the letter of the term that describes a part of a sample with uniform
composition and properties.

a. solution

b. mixture

c. state

d. phase

CHAPTER 2, Matter and Change *(continued)*

6. How many phases exist in these types of mixtures?

   a. Homogeneous _____one_____

   b. Heterogeneous _____two or more_____

▶ Separating Mixtures (pages 46–47)

7. In general, what is used to separate mixtures?

   differences in physical properties

8. The process that separates a solid from a liquid in a heterogeneous mixture is

   called _____filtration_____ .

9. What happens during a distillation?

   A liquid is boiled to produce a vapor that is then condensed into a liquid.

Match each term with its location in the diagram.

   __D__ 15. condenser

   __C__ 16. heat source

   __A__ 17. thermometer

   __B__ 18. tap water

   __E__ 19. distilled water

Reading Skill Practice

By looking carefully at photographs and drawings in textbooks, you can better understand what you have read. Look carefully at Figure 2.8 on page 44. What important idea does this drawing communicate?

This drawing shows that the components of a mixture can be separated based on differences in their physical properties.

SECTION 2.3 ELEMENTS AND COMPOUNDS (pages 48–52)

This section explains a key difference between an element and a compound, and describes how chemical symbols and formulas are used to represent elements and compounds. It also summarizes the process for classifying substances and mixtures.

▶ Distinguishing Elements and Compounds (pages 48–49)

1. All living and nonliving things are made up of building blocks called _____elements_____ .

2. What are the two groups into which substances can be classified?
   Substances can be classified are elements and compounds.
   _____

3. Is the following sentence true or false? Elements can be easily separated into simpler substances. _____false_____

4. Compounds are substances that can be separated into simpler substances only by _____chemical_____ means.

5. Is the following sentence true or false? The properties of compounds are different from those of their component elements. _____true_____

6. Complete this sentence.
   Sodium chloride (table salt) is a _____compound_____ of sodium, which is a soft _____metal_____ , and chlorine, which is a pale yellow _____gas_____ .

▶ Distinguishing Substances and Mixtures (page 50)

7. Describe one way to decide whether a sample of matter is a substance or a mixture.
   If the composition of a sample is fixed, the sample is a substance. If the composition
   of a sample may vary, the sample is a mixture.
   _____

CHAPTER 2, Matter and Change *(continued)*

8. Complete the labels in the diagram below.

▶ **Symbols and Formulas** (pages 51–52)

9. What is used to represent an element?

An element is represented by a one- or two-letter chemical symbol.

_____

10. What are chemical symbols used for?

Chemical symbols are used to write the chemical formulas of compounds.

11. Subscripts in chemical formulas are used to indicate the relative proportions

of the elements in the _____compound_____ .

12. Is the following sentence true or false? The elements that make

up a compound are always present in the same

proportions. _____true_____

13. Use Table 2.2 on page 52 to answer the following questions.

    a. Pb is the symbol for what element? _____ lead _____

    b. What is the symbol for gold? _____ Au _____

    c. Stibium is the Latin name for which element? _____ antimony _____

SECTION 2.4 CHEMICAL REACTIONS (pages 53–55)

This section provides clues to help you recognize a chemical change. It also teaches the law of conservation of mass.

▶ Chemical Changes (page 53)

1. What is a chemical property?

A chemical property is the ability of a substance to undergo a specific
_____

chemical change.
_____

_____

2. Is the following sentence true or false? Chemical properties are observed only

    when a substance undergoes a chemical change. _____ true _____

3. What happens during a chemical reaction?

One or more substances change into one or more new substances.
_____

4. In chemical reactions, the substances present at the start of the reaction are

    called _____ reactants _____ and the substances produced are

    called _____ products _____ .

5. Circle the letter of the term that best completes the sentence. A change in the

    composition of matter _____ occurs during a chemical reaction.

    a. sometimes

    b. rarely

    c. always

    d. never

6. Which representation of a chemical reaction is correct?

    a. products → reactants

    b. reactants → products

CHAPTER 2, Matter and Change *(continued)*

▶ Recognizing Chemical Changes (page 54)

7. List the four possible clues to a chemical change?

transfer of energy, a change in color, the production of a gas, or the formation

of a precipitate

8. Is the following statement true or false? If you observe a clue for chemical change, you can be certain that a chemical change has taken place. _____false_____

9. Define a precipitate.

A precipitate is a solid that forms and settles out of a liquid mixture.

▶ Conservation of Mass (page 55)

10. During a chemical reaction, the mass of the products is always equal to

the mass of the _____reactants_____ .

11. The law of conservation of mass states that in any physical change or

chemical reaction, mass is neither _____created_____ nor

_____destroyed_____ .

12. Look at Figure 2.15 on page 55. How do you know that mass was conserved?

The mass of the product is the same as the mass of the reactants.

3 SCIENTIFIC MEASUREMENT

SECTION 3.1 MEASUREMENTS AND THEIR UNCERTAINTY
(pages 63–72)

This section describes the concepts of accuracy, precision, and error in measurements. It also explains the proper use of significant figures in measurements and calculations.

▶ Using and Expressing Measurements (page 63)

1. Why are numbers used in chemistry often expressed in scientific notation?

   <u>Numbers used in chemical calculations are often very large or very small. Writing</u>

   <u>out all the zeros in such numbers can be very cumbersome. Scientific notation</u>

   <u>makes it easier to work with these numbers.</u>

2. Circle the letter of each sentence that is true about numbers expressed in scientific notation.

   (a.) A number expressed in scientific notation is written as the product of a coefficient and a power of 10.

   (b.) The power of 10 is called the exponent.

   (c.) The coefficient is always a number greater than or equal to one and less than ten.

   d. For numbers less than one, the exponent is positive.

3. Circle the letter of the answer in which 503,000,000 is written correctly in scientific notation.

   a. 5.03×10^{-7}

   b. 503×10^6

   (c.) 5.03×10^8

   d. 503 million

▶ Accuracy, Precision, and Error (pages 64–65)

4. Is the following sentence true or false? To decide whether a measurement has good precision or poor precision, the measurement must be made more than once. <u>true</u>

CHAPTER 3, Scientific Measurement *(continued)*

Label each of the three following sentences that describes accuracy with an *A*. Label each sentence that describes precision with a *P*.

_____P_____ **5.** Four of five repetitions of a measurement were numerically identical, and the fifth varied from the others in value by less than 1%.

_____P_____ **6.** Eight measurements were spread over a wide range.

_____A_____ **7.** A single measurement is within 1% of the correct value.

8. On a dartboard, darts that are closest to the bull's-eye have been thrown with the greatest accuracy. On the second target, draw three darts to represent three tosses of lower precision, but higher accuracy than the darts on the first target.

First target

Second target

9. What is the meaning of "accepted value" with respect to an experimental measurement?

The accepted value is the correct value based on reliable references.

10. Complete the following sentence. For an experimental measurement, the experimental value minus the accepted value is called the _____error_____ .

11. Is the following sentence true or false? The value of an error must be positive. _____false_____

12. Relative error is also called _____percent error_____ .

13. The accepted value of a length measurement is 200 cm, and the experimental value is 198 cm. Circle the letter of the value that shows the percent error of this measurement.

    a. 2%

    b. −2%

    (c.) 1%

    d. −1%

▶ Significant Figures in Measurements (pages 66–67)

14. If a thermometer is calibrated to the nearest degree, to what part of a degree can you estimate the temperature it measures? _____ one tenth of a degree _____

15. Circle the letter of the correct digit. In the measurement 43.52 cm, which digit is the most uncertain?

    a. 4   **c.** 5

    b. 3   (**d.**) 2

16. Circle the letter of the correct number of significant figures in the measurement 6.80 m.

    a. 2   **c.** 4

    (**b.**) 3   **d.** 5

17. List two situations in which measurements have an unlimited number of significant figures.

    a. When the measurement involves counting.

    b. When the measurement involves exactly defined quantities.

    _____

    _____

18. Circle the letter of each sentence that is true about significant figures.

    (**a.**) Every nonzero digit in a reported measurement is assumed to be significant.

    b. Zeros appearing between nonzero digits are never significant.

    (**c.**) Leftmost zeros acting as placeholders in front of nonzero digits in numbers less than one are not significant.

    (**d.**) All rightmost zeros to the right of the decimal point are always significant.

    (**e.**) Zeros to the left of the decimal point that act as placeholders for the first nonzero digit to the left of the decimal point are not significant.

▶ Significant Figures in Calculations (pages 68–71)

19. Is the following sentence true or false? An answer is as precise as the most precise measurement from which it was calculated. _____ false _____

Round the following measurements as indicated.

20. Round 65.145 meters to 4 significant figures. _____ 65.15 meters _____

21. Round 100.1°C to 1 significant figure. _____ 100°C _____

CHAPTER 3, Scientific Measurement *(continued)*

22. Round 155 cm to two significant figures. _____160 cm_____

23. Round 0.000 718 kilograms to two significant figures. ___0.00072 kilograms___

24. Round 65.145 meters to three significant figures. _____65.1 meters_____

SECTION 3.2 THE INTERNATIONAL SYSTEM OF UNITS
(pages 73–79)

This section defines units of measurement for length, volume, mass, temperature, and energy in the International System of Units (SI).

▶ Units and Quantities (pages 74–79)

1. Complete the table showing selected SI base units of measurement.

Units of Measurement		
Quantity	SI base unit	Symbol
Length	meter	m
Mass	kilogram	kg
Temperature	kelvin	K
Time	second	s

2. All metric units of length are based on multiples of __10__ .

3. The International System of Units (SI) is a revised version of the
   _____metric system_____ .

4. Explain what is meant by a "derived unit."
   Derived units are combinations of base units. All SI units are base units, or are
   derived from base units.

5. Give at least one example of a derived unit.
   Students' responses will vary. Possible responses are units of volume, density,
   or speed.

6. Complete the following table showing some metric units of length. Remember that the meter is the SI base unit for length.

Metric Units of Length		
Unit	**Symbol**	**Factor Multiplying Base Unit**
Meter	m	1
Kilometer	km	1000
Centimeter	cm	10^{-2}
Millimeter	mm	10^{-3}
Nanometer	nm	10^{-9}

Match each metric unit with the best estimate of its length or distance.

_____b_____ **7.** Height of a stove top above the floor   **a.** 1 km

_____d_____ **8.** Thickness of about 10 sheets of paper   **b.** 1 m

_____a_____ **9.** Distance along a road spanning about 10 telephone poles   **c.** 1 cm

_____c_____ **10.** Width of a key on a computer keyboard   **d.** 1 mm

11. The space occupied by any sample of matter is called its _____ volume _____.

12. Circle the letter of each sentence that is true about units of volume.

   a. The SI unit for volume is derived from the meter, the SI unit for length.

   b. The liter (L) is a unit of volume.

   c. The liter is an SI unit.

   d. There are 1000 cm^3 in 1 L, and there are also 1000 mL in 1 L, so 1 cm^3 is equal to 1 mL.

Match each of the three descriptions of a volume to the appropriate metric unit of volume.

        Example   **Unit of Volume**

_____b_____ **13.** Interior of an oven   **a.** 1 L

_____a_____ **14.** A box of cookies   **b.** 1 m^3

_____c_____ **15.** One-quarter teaspoon   **c.** 1 mL

CHAPTER 3, Scientific Measurement *(continued)*

16. A volume of 1 L is also equal to

   (a.) 1000 mL

   (b.) 1 dm³

   c. 1000 cm

17. The volume of any solid, liquid, or gas will change with

   _____temperature_____ .

18. A kilogram was originally defined as the mass of _____1 L of liquid water at 4°C_____ .

19. Circle the letter of the unit of mass commonly used in chemistry that equals 1/1000 kilogram.

   (a.) gram   **b.** milligram   **c.** milliliter

Match each unit of mass with the object whose mass would be closest to that unit.

	Mass	Unit of Mass
_c_	**20.** A few grains of sand	**a.** 1 kg
_a_	**21.** A liter bottle of soda	**b.** 1 g
_b_	**22.** Five aspirin tablets	**c.** 1 mg

23. Circle the letter of the instrument shown that is used to measure mass.

   a. scale

   b. balance beam

   (c.) platform balance

   d. analytical balance

24. Is the following sentence true or false? The mass of an object changes with

   location. _____false_____

25. When brought to the surface of the moon, will a mass have more or less weight than it did on the surface of Earth, or will it be the same weight? Explain.

   Its weight will be less, because weight is a measure of gravitational force, and the

   force of gravity on the moon is one-sixth what it is on Earth.

26. Draw an arrow below the diagram, showing the direction of heat transfer between two objects.

lower temperature	higher temperature

27. What properties explain the behavior of liquid-filled thermometers?

Almost all liquids expand in volume with an increase in temperature. This expansion

forces the liquid higher in the thermometer tube as the temperature rises. As the

temperature falls, the liquid contracts and its level in the tube drops.

28. What are the two reference temperatures on the Celsius scale?

The freezing point of water is 0°C and the boiling point of water is 100°C.

29. What is the zero point, 0 K, on the Kelvin scale called?

absolute zero

30. A change of temperature equal to one Kelvin is equal to a change of

temperature of how many degrees Celsius? _____1°C_____

31. Complete the diagram to show the reference temperatures in the Celsius and Kelvin scales.

32. One calorie is the quantity of heat that raises the temperature of

_____1 g_____ of pure water by _____1°C_____ .

SECTION 3.3 CONVERSION PROBLEMS (pages 80–87)

This section explains how to construct conversion factors from equivalent measurements. It also describes how to apply the techniques of dimensional analysis to a variety of conversion problems.

▶ Conversion Factors (pages 80–81)

1. How are the two parts of a conversion factor related?

They are equivalent.

Name _____ Date _____ Class _____

CHAPTER 3, Scientific Measurement *(continued)*

2. Look at Figure 3.11. In a conversion factor, the smaller number is part of the quantity that has the _____larger_____ unit. The larger number is part of the quantity that has the _____smaller_____ unit.

3. Is the following sentence true or false? The actual size of a measurement multiplied by a conversion factor remains the same, because the measurement being converted is multiplied by unity. _____true_____

4. Write two conversion factors based on the relationship between hours and minutes.
$$\frac{60\ minutes}{1\ hour} \text{ and } \frac{1\ hour}{60\ minutes}$$

5. The average lead for a mechanical pencil is 6.0 cm long when it is new. Circle the letter of the conversion factor you would use to find its length in inches.

 a. $\frac{2.54\ cm}{1\ in.}$

 (b.) $\frac{1\ in.}{2.54\ cm}$

 c. $\frac{1\ in.}{6.0\ cm}$

 d. $\frac{6.0\ cm}{1\ in.}$

6. A student is asked to calculate the volume, in milliliters, of 2 cups of oil. There are 225 mL per cup. The student calculates the volume as follows:

$$Volume = 2\ cups \times \frac{1\ cup}{25\ mL} = 0.08\ cup$$

List three errors the student made.

The conversion factor was inverted.

25 mL was used instead of 225 mL.

The unit in the answer is incorrect.

▶ Dimensional Analysis (pages 81–83)

7. What is dimensional analysis?

Dimensional analysis is a way to analyze and solve problems, using the units,

or dimensions, of the measurements.

8. Reread Sample Problem 3.5. The correct conversion factor has the _____known_____ unit in the denominator and the _____unknown_____ unit in the numerator.

26 *Guided Reading and Study Workbook*

© Pearson Education, Inc., publishing as Pearson Prentice Hall. All rights reserved.

9. A container can hold 65 g of water. Circle the conversion factor needed to find the mass of water that 5 identical containers can hold.

a. $\dfrac{5 \text{ containers}}{65 \text{ g water}}$

b. $\dfrac{1 \text{ container}}{65 \text{ g water}}$

c. $\dfrac{65 \text{ g water}}{1 \text{ container}}$

d. $\dfrac{65 \text{ g water}}{5 \text{ containers}}$

▶ Converting Between Units (pages 84–85)

10. Converting between units is easily done using _____ dimensional analysis _____.

11. Circle the letter of the conversion factor that you would use to convert tablespoons to milliliters.

a. $\dfrac{4 \text{ fluid ounces}}{1 \text{ tablespoon}}$

b. $\dfrac{1 \text{ tablespoon}}{4 \text{ fluid ounces}}$

c. $\dfrac{1 \text{ tablespoon}}{15 \text{ mL}}$

d. $\dfrac{15 \text{ mL}}{1 \text{ tablespoon}}$

12. Show the calculation you would use to convert the following:

a. 0.25 m to centimeters

$0.25 \text{ m} \times \dfrac{100 \text{ cm}}{1 \text{ m}}$

b. 9.8 g to kilograms

$9.8 \text{ g} \times \dfrac{1 \text{ kg}}{1000 \text{ g}}$

c. 35 ms to seconds

$35 \text{ ms} \times \dfrac{1 \text{ s}}{1000 \text{ ms}}$

d. 4.2 dL to liters

$4.2 \text{ dL} \times \dfrac{1 \text{ L}}{10 \text{ dL}}$

13. Complex conversions between units may require using _____ more than one _____ conversion factor.

14. How many conversion factors would you need to use to find the number of liters in a cubic decimeter? What are they?

Three conversion factors are needed: $1000 \text{ cm}^3/1 \text{ dm}^3$, $1 \text{ mL}/1 \text{ cm}^3$, $1 \text{ L}/1000 \text{ mL}$

CHAPTER 3, Scientific Measurement *(continued)*

15. How would you calculate the number of nanometers in 8.1 cm?

8.1 cm $\times$ 1 m/10^2 cm $\times$ 10^9 nm/1 m = 8.1 $\times$ 10^7 nm

16. What is the equivalent of 0.35 lb in grams?

0.35 lb $\times$ 1 kg/2.2 lb $\times$ 1000 g/1 kg = 770 g

17. A scientist has 0.46 mL of a solution. How would she convert this volume to microliters?

0.46 mL $\times$ 1 L/10^3 mL $\times$ 10^6 μL/1 L = 460 μL

18. Describe the steps you would use to solve this problem. In a scale drawing of a dining room floor plan, 10 mm equals 2 meters. If the homeowners wanted to purchase flooring that costs $10.89 per square yard, how much would they spend on flooring for the dining room? The dimensions of the dining room on the floor plan are 40 mm $\times$ 32 mm.

1. Convert each dimension to meters, then to yards. 2. Multiply the lengths in yards to

find the number of square yards. 3. Multiply by the cost per yard to find the total cost.

19. Name three common measurements that are expressed as a ratio of two units.

speed, density, gas mileage

20. What technique can be used to convert complex units?

Complex units can be converted using dimensional analysis.

21. A normal concentration of glucose, or sugar, in the blood is 95 mg/dL. How many grams of sugar would be present per liter of blood? Show the conversion factors you use.

95 mg/dL $\times$ 10 dL/1 L $\times$ 1 g/1000 mg = 0.95 g/L

22. Replace each question mark in the table with the conversion factors needed to obtain the given units of density.

Mass	Volume	Density
g	$mm^3 \times$? $\dfrac{1\ m^3}{10^9\ mm^3}$	g/m^3
kg $\times$? $\dfrac{1000\ g}{1\ kg}$	$cm^3 \times$? $\dfrac{1\ m^3}{10^6\ cm^3}$	g/m^3

23. A man can run a mile in 4 minutes. Calculate his average speed in kilometers per hour. Show your work. (1 mile = 1.61 km)

1 mi/4 min $\times$ 1.61 km/1 mi $\times$ 60 min/1 h = 24.2 km/h

24. A baseball player's batting average is .254 (254 hits per 1000 at bats). If she is at bat an average of 3 times per game, how many hits will she make in 52 games? Show your work.

52 games × 3 at bats/1 game × 254 hits/1000 at bats = 39 or 40 hits

SECTION 3.4 DENSITY (pages 89–93)

This section defines density. It explains that density is a characteristic property that depends on the composition of a substance, not on the size of the sample.

▶ Determining Density (page 89–90)

1. Is the mass of one pound of lead greater than, less than, or equal to the mass of one pound of feathers? _____equal to_____

2. Which material has a greater density, lead or feathers? _____lead_____

3. How is density defined?

Density is the ratio of the mass of an object to its volume.

4. The mass of a sample is measured in grams, and its volume is measured in cubic centimeters. In what units would its density be reported?

grams per cubic centimeter (g/cm^3)

5. Look at Table 3.6 on page 90. Circle the letter of the material that will sink in liquid water at 4°C.

a. aluminum

b. corn oil

c. ice

d. gasoline

▶ Density and Temperature (pages 91–92)

6. The density of a substance generally decreases as its temperature increases. Are there any exceptions to this statement? Explain.

Yes. Over a small range of temperatures near the freezing point, the density of water

decreases as the temperature *decreases*. As a result, ice floats on liquid water.

CHAPTER 3, Scientific Measurement *(continued)*

GUIDED PRACTICE PROBLEMS

GUIDED PRACTICE PROBLEM 3 (page 69)

3. Round 87.073 meters to three significant figures. Write your answer in scientific notation.

Step 1. To round to three significant figures, round to the nearest tenth.

87.073 rounds to ___87.1___

Step 2. Write the number in scientific notation.

___8.71×10^1___ meters

GUIDED PRACTICE PROBLEM 34 (page 85)

34. The radius of a potassium atom is 0.227 nm.
Express this radius in centimeters.
Complete the following steps to solve the problem.

Step 1. Use the conversion factors for nanometers and centimeters.

$0.227 \text{ nm} \times \dfrac{1 \text{ m}}{1 \times 10^9 \text{ nm}} \times \dfrac{10^2 \text{ cm}}{1 \text{ m}}$

Step 2. Simplify.

$= \dfrac{0.227 \times 10^2}{10^9}$ centimeter

Step 3. Divide.

$= 2.27 \times 10^{-8}$ cm

EXTRA PRACTICE (similar to Practice Problem 36, page 86)

36. Gold has a density of about 20 g/cm³. Estimate this density in kg/m³.

$\dfrac{20 \text{ g}}{1 \text{ cm}^3} \times \dfrac{1 \text{ kg}}{10^3 \text{ g}} \times \dfrac{(10^2 \text{ cm})^3}{1 \text{ m}^3} = \dfrac{20 \times 10^6 \text{ kg}}{10^3 \text{ m}^3} = \dfrac{2.0 \times 10^7 \text{ kg}}{10^3 \text{ m}^3}$

$= 2.0 \times 10^4 \text{ kg/m}^3$

GUIDED PRACTICE PROBLEM 46 (page 91)

46. A student finds a shiny piece of metal that she thinks is aluminum. In the lab, she determines that the metal has a volume of 245 cm^3 and a mass of 612 g. Calculate the density. Is the metal aluminum?

Analyze

Step 1. List the known values.

Volume = 245 cm^3

Mass = ___612___ g

Step 2. List the unknown.

_____density_____

Calculate

Step 3. Use the following relationship to find the density. Remember to round your answer to three significant figures.

$$\text{Density} = \frac{\text{mass}}{\text{volume}}$$

$$= \frac{612 \text{ g}}{245 \text{ cm}^3}$$

$$= \underline{2.50} \text{ g/cm}^3$$

Step 4. To determine whether the piece of metal is aluminum, compare the density of the metal to the density of aluminum given in Table 3.7 on page 90. Is the metal aluminum? _____no_____

Evaluate

Step 5. Underline the correct word(s) that complete(s) this statement. Because the mass of the metal is about two and one-half times the volume, a density of about 2.5 g/cm^3 is reasonable. Because a density of 2.50 g/cm^3 is nearly 10% less than 2.7 g/cm^3, the density of aluminum, the metal (is, is not) aluminum.

EXTRA PRACTICE (similar to Practice Problem 48a, page 92)

48a. Use dimensional analysis to convert 4.68 g of boron to cubic centimeters of boron. The density of boron is 2.34 g/cm^3.

$$4.68 \text{ g of boron} \div \frac{2.34 \text{ g}}{\text{cm}^3} = 4.68 \text{ g} \times \frac{1 \text{ cm}^3}{2.34 \text{ g}}$$

$$= 2 \text{ cm}^3 \text{ of boron}$$

ATOMIC STRUCTURE

SECTION 4.1 DEFINING THE ATOM (pages 101–103)

This section describes early atomic theories of matter and provides ways to understand the tiny size of individual atoms.

▶ Early Models of the Atom (pages 101–102)

1. Democritus, who lived in Greece during the fourth century B.C., suggested that matter is made up of tiny particles that cannot be divided. He called these particles _____atoms_____ .

2. List two reasons why the ideas of Democritus were not useful in a scientific sense. They did not explain chemical behavior, and they lacked experimental support because Democritus's approach was not based on the scientific method.

3. The modern process of discovery about atoms began with the theories of an English schoolteacher named _____John Dalton_____ .

4. Circle the letter of each sentence that is true about Dalton's atomic theory.

   (a.) All elements are composed of tiny, indivisible particles called atoms.

   b. An element is composed of several types of atoms.

   (c.) Atoms of different elements can physically mix together, or can chemically combine in simple, whole-number ratios to form compounds.

   (d.) Chemical reactions occur when atoms are separated, joined, or rearranged; however, atoms of one element are never changed into atoms of another element by a chemical reaction.

5. In the diagram, use the labels *mixture* and *compound* to identify the mixture of elements A and B and the compound that forms when the atoms of elements A and B combine chemically.

(a) Atoms of element A

(b) Atoms of element B

compound

mixture

CHAPTER 4, Atomic Structure *(continued)*

▶ Sizing up the Atom (page 103)

6. Suppose you could grind a sample of the element copper into smaller and smaller particles. The smallest particle that could no longer be divided, yet still has the chemical properties of copper, is ___an atom of copper___ .

7. About how many atoms of copper when placed side by side would form a line 1 cm long? ___100,000,000___

SECTION 4.2 STRUCTURE OF THE NUCLEAR ATOM (pages 104–108)

This section describes the experiments that led to the discovery of subatomic particles and their properties.

▶ Subatomic Particles (pages 104–106)

1. How is the atomic theory that is accepted today different from Dalton's atomic theory? ___Atoms are now known to be divisible. They can be broken down into even smaller, more fundamental particles.___

2. Which subatomic particles carry a negative charge? ___electrons___

Match each term from the experiments of J. J. Thomson with the correct description.

___c___ **3.** anode

     a. an electrode with a negative charge

___a___ **4.** cathode

     b. a glowing beam traveling between charged electrodes

___b___ **5.** cathode ray

     c. an electrode with a positive charge

___d___ **6.** electron

     d. a negatively charged particle

7. The diagram shows electrons moving from left to right in a cathode-ray tube. Draw an arrow showing how the path of the electrons will be affected by the placement of the negatively and positively charged plates.

8. Thomson observed that the production of cathode rays did not depend on the kind of gas in the tube or the type of metal used for the electrodes. What conclusion did he draw from these observations?

He concluded that electrons must be parts of the atoms of all elements.

9. What two properties of an electron did Robert Millikan determine from his experiments?

He determined the quantity of charge carried by an electron and its mass.

10. Circle the letter of each sentence that is true about atoms, matter, and electric charge.

a. All atoms have an electric charge.

b. Electric charges are carried by particles of matter.

c. Electric charges always exist in whole-number multiples of a single basic unit.

d. When a given number of positively charged particles combines with an equal number of negatively charged particles, an electrically neutral particle is formed.

11. Circle the letter next to the number of units of positive charge that remain if a hydrogen atom loses an electron.

a. 0   **b.** 1   **c.** 2   **d.** 3

12. The positively charged subatomic particle that remains when a hydrogen atom loses an electron is called _____a proton_____ .

13. What charge does a neutron carry? _____none_____ .

14. Complete the table about the properties of subatomic particles.

Properties of Subatomic Particles				
Particle	**Symbol**	**Relative Electrical Charge**	**Relative Mass** (mass of proton = 1)	**Actual Mass** (g)
Electron	e^-	$1-$	$\dfrac{1}{1840}$	9.11×10^{-28}
Proton	p^+	$1+$	1	1.67×10^{-24}
Neutron	n^0	0	1	1.67×10^{-24}

CHAPTER 4, Atomic Structure *(continued)*

▶ **The Atomic Nucleus** (pages 106–108)

15. Is the following sentence true or false? An alpha particle has a double positive charge because it is a helium atom that has lost two electrons. _____ true _____

16. Explain why in 1911 Rutherford and his coworkers were surprised when they shot a narrow beam of alpha particles through a thin sheet of gold foil.

They expected most of the alpha particles to pass easily through the foil with only a

slight deflection. They found that most alpha particles were not deflected at all, and

a few were deflected at very large angles.

_____

_____

17. Circle the letter of each sentence that is true about the nuclear theory of atoms suggested by Rutherford's experimental results.

(a.) An atom is mostly empty space.

(b.) All the positive charge of an atom is concentrated in a small central region called the nucleus.

c. The nucleus is composed of protons.

d. The nucleus is large compared with the atom as a whole.

(e.) Nearly all the mass of an atom is in its nucleus.

SECTION 4.3 DISTINGUISHING AMONG ATOMS (pages 110–119)

This section explains how atomic number identifies an element; how to use atomic number and mass number to find the number of protons, neutrons, and electrons in an atom; how isotopes differ; and how to calculate average atomic mass.

▶ **Atomic Number** (page 110)

1. Circle the letter of the term that correctly completes the sentence. Elements are different because their atoms contain different numbers of _____ .

a. electrons

(b.) protons

c. neutrons

d. nuclei

Name _____ Date _____ Class _____

2. Complete the table showing the number of protons and electrons in atoms of six elements.

Atoms of Six Elements				
Name	**Symbol**	**Atomic Number**	**Number of Protons**	**Number of Electrons**
Hydrogen	H	1	1	1
Helium	He	2	2	2
Lithium	Li	3	3	3
Boron	B	5	5	5
Carbon	C	6	6	6
Oxygen	O	8	8	8

▶ **Mass Number** (pages 111–112)

3. The total number of protons and neutrons in an atom is its _____mass number_____ .

4. What is the mass number of a helium atom that has two protons and two neutrons? _____4_____

5. How many neutrons does a beryllium atom with four protons and a mass number of nine have? _____5_____

6. Place the labels *chemical symbol*, *atomic number*, and *mass number* in the shorthand notation below.

7. Designate the atom shown in Question 6 in the form "name of element"-"mass number." _____neon-22_____

8. How many protons, neutrons, and electrons are in the atom discussed in Questions 6 and 7? Protons: [10] Neutrons: [12] Electrons: [10]

CHAPTER 4, Atomic Structure *(continued)*

▶ Isotopes (pages 112–113)

9. How do atoms of neon-20 and neon-22 differ?

   An atom of neon-22 has two more neutrons in its nucleus than an atom of neon-20.

   _____

10. Neon-20 and neon-22 are called _____isotopes_____ .

11. Is the following sentence true or false? Isotopes are chemically alike because they have identical numbers of protons and electrons. _____true_____

Match the designation of each hydrogen isotope with its commonly used name.

   ___b___ 12. hydrogen-1   **a.** tritium

   ___c___ 13. hydrogen-2   **b.** hydrogen

   ___a___ 14. hydrogen-3   **c.** deuterium

▶ Atomic Mass (pages 114–117)

15. Why is the atomic mass unit (amu), rather than the gram, usually used to express atomic mass?

    The values of atomic masses measured in grams are inconveniently small and

    impractical to work with.

16. What isotope of carbon has been chosen as the reference isotope for atomic mass units? What is the defined atomic mass in amu of this isotope?

    carbon-12; 12 amu

17. Is the following sentence true or false? The atomic mass of an element is always a whole number of atomic mass units. _____false_____

18. Circle the letter of each statement that is true about the average atomic mass of an element and the relative abundance of its isotopes.

    (a.) In nature, most elements occur as a mixture of two or more isotopes.

    b. Isotopes of an element do not have a specific natural percent abundance.

    (c.) The average atomic mass of an element is usually closest to that of the isotope with the highest natural abundance.

    d. Because hydrogen has three isotopes with atomic masses of about 1 amu, 2 amu, and 3 amu, respectively, the average atomic mass of natural hydrogen is 2 amu.

19. Circle the letter of the correct answer. When chlorine occurs in nature, there are three atoms of chlorine-35 for every one atom of chlorine-37. Which atomic mass number is closer to the average atomic mass of chlorine?

    (a.) 35 amu   **b.** 37 amu

20. In the periodic table, the elements are organized into groups based on

a set of repeating properties
_____ .

▶ **The Periodic Table—A Preview (page 118)**

21. What are the horizontal rows in the periodic table called?

periods
_____

📖 Reading Skill Practice

Outlining can help you understand and remember what you have read. Prepare an outline of Section 4.3, *Distinguishing Among Atoms.* Begin with the headings in the textbook. Under each heading, write the main idea. Then list the details that support the main idea. Do your work on a separate sheet of paper.

Main heads should be Atomic Number, Mass Number, Isotopes, and Atomic Mass. Subheads should indicate an understanding of each concept.

CHAPTER 4, Atomic Structure *(continued)*

GUIDED PRACTICE PROBLEMS

Fill in the write-on lines and boxes provided as you work through the guided practice problems.

GUIDED PRACTICE PROBLEM 18 (page 112)

18. Use Table 4.2 to express the compositions of carbon-12, fluorine-19, and beryllium-9 in shorthand notation.

Analyze

Carbon-12

Step 1. The number of protons in an atom is called its _____atomic_____ number.

The number of protons in an atom of carbon-12 is ____6____ .

Calculate

Step 2. The number of protons plus the number of neutrons in an atom is called its _____mass_____ number. For carbon-12, this number is ____12____ .

Step 3. The shorthand notation for carbon-12 is:

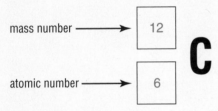

Evaluate

Step 4. Except for hydrogen-1, the mass number of an isotope is always greater than its atomic number. Is the mass number reasonable? ____yes____

Fluorine-19

Step 1. The atomic number of fluorine-19 is ____9____ .

Step 2. Its mass number is ____19____ .

Step 3. The shorthand notation for fluorine-19 is:

Step 4. Is your answer reasonable? Why?

Yes it is, because the mass number is greater than the atomic number.

_____

Beryllium-9

Step 1. The atomic number of beryllium-9 is _____4_____ .

Step 2. Its mass number is _____9_____ .

Step 3. The shorthand notation for beryllium-9 is:

Step 4. Is your answer reasonable? Why?

Yes it is, because the mass number is greater than the atomic number.

EXTRA PRACTICE (similar to Practice Problem 19, page 113)

19. Three isotopes of sulfur are sulfur-32, sulfur-33, and sulfur-34. Write the complete symbol for each isotope, including the atomic number and the mass number.

sulfur-32   sulfur-33   sulfur-34

GUIDED PRACTICE PROBLEM 23 (page 117)

23. The element copper has naturally occurring isotopes with mass numbers of 63 and 65. The relative abundance and atomic masses are 69.2% for mass = 62.93 amu and 30.8% for mass = 64.93 amu. Calculate the average atomic mass of copper.

Analyze

Step 1. Will the average atomic mass be closer to 63 or to 65? Explain.

Because about 70% of the element consists of the lighter isotope, the average atomic

mass should be closer to the atomic mass number of 63 than 65.

Solve

Step 2. For Cu-63: 69.2% × 62.93 amu = 0.692 × 62.93 amu = 43.6 amu

Step 3. For Cu-65: 30.8% × 64.93 amu = 0.308 × 64.93 amu = 20.0 amu

Step 4. Average mass: 43.6 amu + 20.0 amu = 63.6 amu

Evaluate

Step 5. Explain why your answer is reasonable.

It is closer to 63 than 65.

Name _____ Date _____ Class _____

CHAPTER 4, Atomic Structure *(continued)*

EXTRA PRACTICE (similar to Practice Problem 24, page 117)

24. Calculate the atomic mass of rubidium. The two isotopes of rubidium
have atomic masses and relative abundancies of 84.91 amu (72.16%)
and 86.91 amu (27.84%). _____ 85.47 amu _____

5 ELECTRONS IN ATOMS

SECTION 5.1 MODELS OF THE ATOM (pages 127–132)

This section summarizes the development of atomic theory. It also explains the significance of quantized energies of electrons as they relate to the quantum mechanical model of the atom.

▶ The Development of Atomic Models (pages 127–128)

1. Complete the table about atomic models and the scientists who developed them.

Scientist	Model of Atom
Dalton	The atom is a solid indivisible mass.
Thomson	The atom is a ball of positive charge with electrons stuck into the ball.
Rutherford	Most of an atom's mass is concentrated in the small, positively charged nucleus. The electrons surround the nucleus and the rest of the atom is empty space.
Bohr	Electrons are arranged in concentric circular paths around the nucleus.

2. Is the following sentence true or false? The electrons in an atom can exist between energy levels: _____ false _____

▶ The Bohr Model (pages 128–129)

3. What is a small, discrete unit of energy called?

It is called a quantum.

4. Circle the letter of the term that completes the sentence correctly. A quantum of energy is the amount of energy required to

   a. move an electron from its present energy level to the next lower one

   b. maintain an electron in its present energy level

   c. move an electron from its present energy level to the next higher one

5. In general, the higher the electron is on the energy ladder, the

_____ farther _____ it is from the nucleus.

CHAPTER 5, Electrons in Atoms *(continued)*

▶ The Quantum Mechanical Model (page 130)

6. What is the difference between the previous models of the atom and the modern quantum mechanical model? Previous models described the motion of electrons the same way as the motion of large objects. The quantum mechanical model is not based on the exact path an electron follows around the nucleus.

7. Is the following sentence true or false? The quantum mechanical model of the atom estimates the probability of finding an electron in a certain position. true

▶ Atomic Orbitals (pages 131–132)

8. Circle the letter of the term that correctly answers this question. Which name describes the major energy levels of electrons?

   a. atomic orbitals   b. quantum mechanical numbers

   c. quantas   d. principal quantum numbers (n)

9. Principal energy levels are assigned values in order of generally increasing energy: $n = 1, 2, 3, 4$, and so forth.

10. In the quantum mechanical model the regions where electrons are likely to be found are called atomic orbitals and are denoted by letters .

11. Match each diagram below with the name of its p orbital, the p_x, p_y, or p_z.

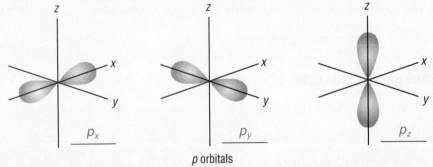

p orbitals

12. Use the diagram above. Describe how the p_x, p_y, and p_z orbitals are similar. The p orbitals are similar because they are all dumbbell shaped.

13. Describe how the p_x, p_y, and p_z orbitals are different. The p orbitals have different orientations in space. They are all perpendicular to each other.

14. Circle the letter of the formula for the maximum number of electrons that can occupy a principal energy level. Use n for the principal quantum number.

   a. $2n^2$ b. n^2 c. $2n$ d. n

SECTION 5.2 ELECTRON ARRANGEMENT IN ATOMS (pages 133–136)

This section shows you how to apply the aufbau principle, the Pauli exclusion principle, and Hund's rule to help you write the electron configurations of elements. It also explains why the electron configurations for some elements differ from those assigned using the aufbau principle.

▶ Electron Configurations (pages 133–135)

1. The ways in which electrons are arranged around the nuclei of atoms are called _____ electron configurations _____ .

Match the name of the rule used to find the electron configurations of atoms with the rule itself.

__b__ 2. aufbau principle

__c__ 3. Pauli exclusion principle

__a__ 4. Hund's rule

a. When electrons occupy orbitals of equal energy, one electron enters each orbital until all the orbitals contain one electron with parallel spins.

b. Electrons enter orbitals of lowest energy first.

c. An atomic orbital may describe at most two electrons.

5. Look at the aufbau diagram, Figure 5.7 on page 133. Which atomic orbital is of higher energy, a 4f or a 5p orbital? __4f__

6. Fill in the electron configurations for the elements given in the table. Use the orbital filling diagrams to complete the table.

Electron Configurations for Some Selected Elements							
	Orbital filling						Electron configuration
Element	1s	2s	2p_x	2p_y	2p_z	3s	
H	↑						$1s^1$
He	↑↓						$1s^2$
Li	↑↓	↑					$1s^2 2s^1$
C	↑↓	↑↓	↑	↑			$1s^2 2s^2 2p^2$
N	↑↓	↑↓	↑	↑	↑		$1s^2 2s^2 2p^3$
O	↑↓	↑↓	↑↓	↑	↑		$1s^2 2s^2 2p^4$
F	↑↓	↑↓	↑↓	↑↓	↑		$1s^2 2s^2 2p^5$
Ne	↑↓	↑↓	↑↓	↑↓	↑↓		$1s^2 2s^2 2p^6$
Na	↑↓	↑↓	↑↓	↑↓	↑↓	↑	$1s^2 2s^2 2p^6 3s^1$

CHAPTER 5, Electrons in Atoms *(continued)*

7. In the shorthand method for writing an electron configuration, what does a superscript stand for?

The superscript stands for the number of electrons occupying a given sublevel.

8. In the shorthand method for writing an electron configuration, what does the sum of the superscripts equal?

The sum equals the number of electrons in the atom.

▶ Exceptional Electron Configurations (page 136)

9. Is the following sentence true or false? The aufbau principle works for every element in the periodic table. _____false_____

10. Filled energy sublevels are more _____stable_____ than partially filled sublevels.

11. Half-filled levels are not as stable as _____filled_____ levels, but are more stable than other configurations.

 # Reading Skill Practice

Outlining can help you understand and remember what you have read. Prepare an outline of Section 5.2, *Electron Arrangement in Atoms.* Begin your outline by copying the headings from the textbook. Under each heading, write the main idea. Then list the details that support, or back up, the main idea. Do your work on a separate sheet of paper.

The subheads of students' outlines of the section should be Electron Configurations and Exceptional Electron Configurations. The section's main ideas should form the next level of the outline.

SECTION 5.3 PHYSICS AND THE QUANTUM MECHANICAL MODEL (pages 138–146)

This section explains how to calculate the wavelength, frequency, or energy of light, given two of these values. It also explains the origin of the atomic emission spectrum of an element.

▶ Light (pages 138–140)

1. Match each term describing waves to its definition.

__b__	amplitude	**a.** the distance between two crests
__a__	wavelength	**b.** the wave's height from the origin to the crest
__c__	frequency	**c.** the number of wave cycles to pass a given point per unit of time

2. The units of frequency are usually cycles per second. The SI unit of cycles per second is called a(n) _____hertz (Hz)_____ .

3. Label the parts of a wave in this drawing. Label the wavelength, the amplitude, the crest, and the origin.

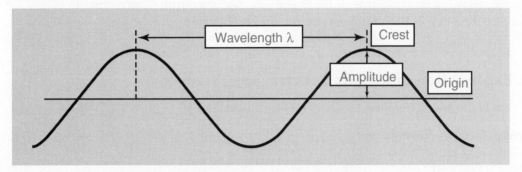

4. The product of wavelength and frequency always equals a(n) _____constant_____ , the speed of light.

5. Is the following sentence true or false? The wavelength and frequency of all waves are inversely proportional to each other. _____true_____

6. Light consists of electromagnetic waves. What kinds of visible and invisible radiation are included in the electromagnetic spectrum?

The following kinds of radiation are included in the electromagnetic spectrum: radio

waves, microwaves, infrared waves, visible light, ultraviolet waves, x-ray, and gamma

rays.

7. When sunlight passes through a prism, the different wavelengths separate into a(n) _____spectrum_____ of colors.

8. Put the visible colors in order of frequency.

_____2_____ orange   _____6_____ violet
_____4_____ green   _____3_____ yellow
_____5_____ blue   _____1_____ red

9. Look at Figure 5.10 on page 139. The electromagnetic spectrum consists of radiation over a broad band of wavelengths. What type of radiation has the lowest frequency? The highest frequency?

Radio waves have the lowest frequency. Gamma rays have the highest frequency.

▶ Atomic Spectra (page 141)

10. What happens when an electric current is passed through the gas or vapor of an element?

The element emits light as it is excited by the passage of the electric current.

CHAPTER 5, Electrons in Atoms *(continued)*

11. Passing the light emitted by an element through a prism gives the
_____atomic emission spectrum_____ of the element.

12. Is the following sentence true or false? The emission spectrum of an element can be the same as the emission spectrum of another element.
_____false_____

▶ An Explanation of Atomic Spectra *(pages 142–143)*

13. What is the lowest possible energy of an electron called? _____ground state_____

14. Only electrons moving from _____higher_____ to
_____lower_____ energy levels lose energy and emit light.

▶ Quantum Mechanics *(pages 381–382)*

15. What did Albert Einstein call the quanta of energy that is light?
_____photons_____

16. What did de Broglie's equation predict about the behavior of particles?
It predicts that all moving objects have wavelike motions.

17. Is the following sentence true or false? The new method of describing the motions of subatomic particles, atoms, and molecules is called quantum mechanics. _____true_____

18. Is the following sentence true or false? de Broglie's conclusions were supported by experimental evidence. _____true_____

19. Does the Heisenberg uncertainty principle apply to cars and airplanes?
No, only to small particles.

GUIDED PRACTICE PROBLEM

GUIDED PRACTICE PROBLEM 14 (page 140)

14. What is the wavelength of radiation with a frequency of 1.50×10^{13} Hz ($1.50 \times 10^{13} s^{-1}$)? Does this radiation have a longer or shorter wavelength than red light?

Analyze

Step 1. What is the equation for the relationship between frequency and wavelength? _____ $c = \lambda \upsilon$ _____

Step 2. What does c represent and what is its value?

It represents the speed of light, which is 3.00×10^8 m/s.

Step 3. What is the wavelength of red light in cm?

Red light has a wavelength of about 700 nm, which can be converted to m by

dividing by 10^9 nm/m, producing 7×10^{-7} m.

Solve

Step 4. Solve the equation for the unknown. $\lambda = \underline{\dfrac{c}{\upsilon}}$

Step 5. Substitute the known quantities into the equation and solve.

$$\dfrac{3.00 \times 10^8 \text{ m/s}}{1.50 \times 10^{13} \text{ s}} = \boxed{2.00 \times 10^{-5} \text{ m}}$$

Step 6. Compare the answer with the wavelength of red light. Does the given radiation have a wavelength longer or shorter than that of red light?

The answer, 2.00×10^{-5} m, is greater than the wavelength of red light, 7×10^{-7} m.

Therefore, this radiation has a longer wavelength than red light.

Evaluate

Step 7. Explain why you think your result makes sense?

The magnitude of the frequency is about 10^5 times the magnitude of c. Because

frequency and wavelength are inversely proportional to each other, the answer

should be about 10^{-5}.

Step 8. Are the units in your answer correct? How do you know?

Yes, because wavelength is measured in meters or fractions of a meter.

THE PERIODIC TABLE

6

SECTION 6.1 ORGANIZING THE ELEMENTS (pages 155–160)

This section describes the development of the periodic table and explains the periodic law. It also describes the classification of elements into metals, nonmetals, and metalloids.

▶ Searching For An Organizing Principle (page 155)

1. How many elements had been identified by the year 1700? _____13_____

2. What caused the rate of discovery to increase after 1700?

Chemists began to use scientific methods to search for elements.

_____

3. What did chemists use to sort elements into groups?

Chemists used the properties of elements.

_____

▶ Mendeleev's Periodic Table (page 156)

4. Who was Dmitri Mendeleev? Dmitri Mendeleev was a Russian chemist and teacher

who developed a periodic table of elements.

5. What property did Mendeleev use to organize the elements into a periodic table?

Mendeleev arranged the elements in order of increasing atomic mass.

6. Is the following sentence true or false? Mendeleev used his periodic table to

predict the properties of undiscovered elements. _____true_____

▶ The Periodic Law (page 157)

7. How are the elements arranged in the modern periodic table?

The elements are arranged in order by increasing atomic number.

8. Is the following statement true or false? The periodic law states that when

elements are arranged in order of increasing atomic number, there is a

periodic repetition of physical and chemical properties. _____true_____

▶ Metals, Nonmetals, and Metalloids (pages 158–160)

9. Explain the color coding of the squares in the periodic table in Figure 6.5.

Yellow squares contain metals, blue squares contain nonmetals, green squares

contain metalloids.

CHAPTER 6, The Periodic Table *(continued)*

10. Which property below is not a general property of metals.

    a. ductile   **c.** malleable

    b. poor conductor of heat   **d.** high luster

11. Is the following statement true or false? The variation in properties among metals is greater than the variation in properties among nonmetals. _____false_____

12. Under some conditions, a metalloid may behave like a _____metal_____ .

    Under other conditions, a metalloid may behave like a _____nonmetal_____ .

SECTION 6.2 CLASSIFYING THE ELEMENTS (pages 161–167)

This section explains why you can infer the properties of an element based on the properties of other elements in the periodic table. It also describes the use of electron configurations to classify elements.

▶ **Squares In The Periodic Table** (pages 161–163)

1. Label the sample square from the periodic table below. Use the labels *element name, element symbol, atomic number,* and *average atomic mass.*

2. List three things, other than the name, symbol, atomic number, and average atomic mass, you can discover about an element using the periodic table in Figure 6.9.

    a. state at room temperature

    b. electrons in each energy level

    c. whether an element is found in nature

▶ **Electron Configurations In Groups** (pages 164–165)

3. Is the following sentence true or false? The subatomic particles that play the key role in determining the properties of an element are electrons. _____true_____

4. Why are Group A elements called representative elements?

    They exhibit a wide range of physical and chemical properties.

    _____

5. Classify each of the following elements as a (an) *alkali metal, alkaline earth metal, halogen,* or *noble gas.*

a. sodium _____alkali metal_____   e. xenon _____noble gas_____

b. chlorine _____halogen_____   f. potassium _____alkali metal_____

c. calcium _____alkaline earth metal_____   g. magnesium _____alkaline earth metal_____

d. fluorine _____halogen_____

6. For elements in each of the following groups, how many electrons are in the highest occupied energy level?

a. Group 3A _____3_____

b. Group 1A _____1_____

c. Group 8A _____8_____

▶ **Transition Elements** (page 166)

7. Complete the table about classifying elements according to the electron configuration of their highest occupied energy level.

Category	Description of Electron Configuration
Noble gases	*s* or *p* sublevels are filled
Representative elements	*s* or *p* sublevels are only partially filled
Transition metals	*s* sublevel and nearby *d* sublevel contain electrons
Inner transition metals	*s* sublevel and nearby *f* sublevel contain electrons

8. Circle the letter of the elements found in the *p* block.

a. Groups 1A and 2A and helium

b. Groups 3A, 4A, 5A, 6A, 7A, and 8A except for helium

c. transition metals

d. inner transition metals

Match the category of elements with an element from that category.

__c__   **9.** Noble gases   **a.** gallium

__a__   **10.** Representative elements   **b.** nobelium

__d__   **11.** Transition metals   **c.** argon

__b__   **12.** Inner transition metals   **d.** vanadium

CHAPTER 6, The Periodic Table *(continued)*

13. Use Figure 6.12 on page 166. Write the electron configurations for the following elements.

   a. magnesium _____ $1s^22s^22p^63s^2$ _____

   b. cobalt _____ $1s^22s^22p^63s^23p^63d^74s^2$ _____

   c. sulfur _____ $1s^22s^22p^63s^23p^4$ _____

SECTION 6.3 PERIODIC TRENDS (pages 170–178)

This section explains how to interpret group trends and periodic trends in atomic size, ionization energy, ionic size, and electronegativity.

▶ Trends in Atomic Size (pages 170–171)

1. Is the following sentence true or false? The radius of an atom can be measured

   directly. _____ false _____

2. What are the atomic radii for the following molecules?

Hydrogen	**Oxygen**	**Nitrogen**	**Chlorine**
atomic radius =	atomic radius =	atomic radius =	atomic radius =
30 pm	68 pm	70 pm	102 pm

3. What is the general trend in atomic size within a group? Within a period?

   The atomic size increases within a group as atomic number increases. The atomic

   size decreases from left to right across a period.

4. What are the two variables that affect atomic size within a group?

   a. the charge on the nucleus _____

   b. the number of occupied energy levels _____

5. For each pair of elements, pick the element with the largest atom.

   a. Helium and argon _____ argon _____

   b. Potassium and argon _____ potassium _____

▶ Ions (page 172)

6. What is an ion?

   An ion is an atom or group of atoms that has a positive or negative charge.

7. How are ions formed?

An ion is formed when electrons are transferred between atoms.

8. An ion with a positive charge is called a(n) _____anion_____ ; an ion with a negative charge is called a(n) _____cation_____ .

9. Complete the table about anions and cations.

	Anions	**Cations**
Charge	negative	positive
Metal/Nonmetal	nonmetal	metal
Minus sign/Plus sign	plus sign	minus sign

▶ Trends in Ionization Energy (pages 173–175)

10. _____Ionization energy_____ is the energy required to overcome the attraction of protons in the nucleus and remove an electron from a gaseous atom.

11. Why does ionization energy tend to decrease from top to bottom within a group?

Atomic size increases from top to bottom within the group. The nuclear charge has a smaller effect on the electrons in the highest occupied energy level and less energy is required to remove an electron.

12. Why does ionization energy tend to increase as you move across a period?

The nuclear charge increases across a period but the shielding effect remains constant. There is greater attraction of the electrons to the nucleus and more energy is required to remove an electron. Atomic size increases from top to bottom within the group.

13. There is a large increase in ionization energy between the second and the third ionization energies of a metal. What kind of ion is the metal likely to form? Include the charge in your answer.

an ion with a 2+ charge

▶ Trends in Ionic Size (page 176)

14. Metallic elements tend to _____lose_____ electrons and form _____positive_____ ions.

Nonmetallic elements tend to _____gain_____ electrons and form _____negative_____ ions.

CHAPTER 6, The Periodic Table *(continued)*

15. Circle the letter of the statement that is true about ion size.

    (**a.**) Cations are always smaller than the neutral atoms from which they form.

    b. Anions are always smaller than the neutral atoms from which they form.

    c. Within a period, a cation with a greater charge has a larger ionic radius.

    d. Within a group, a cation with a higher atomic number has a smaller ionic radius.

16. Which ion has the larger ionic radius: Ca^{2+} or Cl^-? ____Cl^-____

▶ Trends in Electronegativity (page 177)

17. What property of an element represents its tendency to attract electrons when it chemically combines with another element? _____electronegativity_____

18. Use Table 6.2 on page 177. What trend do you see in the relative electronegativity values of elements within a group? Within a period?

The electronegativity values decrease as you move down a group, but increase as

you move across a period.

19. Circle the letter of each statement that is true about electronegativity values.

    a. The electronegativity values of the transition elements are all zero.

    b. The element with the highest electronegativity value is sodium.

    (**c.**) Nonmetals have higher electronegativity values than metals.

    (**d.**) Electronegativity values can help predict the types of bonds atoms form.

▶ Summary of Trends (page 178)

20. Use Figure 6.22 on page 178. Circle the letter of each property for which aluminum has a higher value than silicon.

    (**a.**) first ionization energy   **c.** electronegativity

    (**b.**) atomic radius   **d.** ionic radius

 # Reading Skill Practice

A graph can help you understand comparisons of data at a glance. Use graph paper to make a graph of the data in Table 6.2 on page 177. Plot electronegativity values on the vertical axis. Use a range from 0 to 4. Plot atomic number on the horizontal axis. Label each period and the first element in each period.

Students' graphs should show a trend of increasing electronegativity values within a period as atomic number increases, and a dramatic decrease in the electronegativity value between the Group 7A element in one period and the group 1A element in the next period.

GUIDED PRACTICE PROBLEM

GUIDED PRACTICE PROBLEM 8 (page 167)

8. Use Figure 6.9 and Figure 6.12 to write the electron configurations of these elements.

   a. carbon   **b.** strontium   **c.** vanadium

Analyze

a. What is the number of electrons for each element?

C ___6___   Sr ___38___   V ___23___

b. What is the highest occupied energy sublevel for each element, according to its position on the periodic table? Remember that the energy level for the *d* block is always one less than the period.

C ___2p___   Sr ___5s___   V ___3d___

c. According to its position on the periodic table, how many electrons does each element have in the sublevel listed above?

C ___2___   Sr ___2___   V ___3___

Solve

d. Begin filling in electron sublevels. Start from the top left and move right across each period in Figure 6.12 until you reach the highest occupied sublevel for each element. Make sure the *d*-block is in the correct energy level.

C ___$1s^2 2s^2 2p^2$___   Sr ___$1s^2 2s^2 2p^6 3s^2 3p^6 3d^{10} 4s^2 4p^6 5s^2$___

V ___$1s^2 2s^2 2p^6 3s^2 3p^6 3d^3 4s^2$___

e. How can you check whether your answers are correct?

Add all the superscripts in the electron configurations. This sum should be equal to the atomic number for that element.

f. Check your answers as outlined above.

C ___$2 + 2 + 2 = 6$, equal to the atomic number___

Sr ___$2 + 2 + 6 + 2 + 6 + 10 + 2 + 6 + 2 = 38$, equal to the atomic number___

V ___$2 + 2 + 6 + 2 + 6 + 3 + 2 = 23$, equal to the atomic number___

7 IONIC AND METALLIC BONDING

SECTION 7.1 IONS (pages 187–193)

This section explains how to use the periodic table to infer the number of valence electrons in an atom and draw its electron dot structure. It also describes the formation of cations from metals and anions from nonmetals.

▶ Valence Electrons (pages 187–188)

1. What are valence electrons? Valence electrons are the electrons in the highest occupied energy level of an element's atoms.

2. The valence electrons largely determine the ___chemical properties___ of an element and are usually the only electrons used in ___chemical bonds___ .

3. Is the following sentence true or false? The group number of an element in the periodic table is related to the number of valence electrons it has. ___true___

4. What is an electron dot structure? It is a diagram that shows the valence electrons as dots.

5. Draw the electron dot structure of each of the following atoms.

   a. argon _____ $: \overset{..}{\underset{..}{Ar}} :$

   b. calcium _____ $\cdot Ca \cdot$

   c. iodine _____ $: \overset{..}{\underset{..}{I}} \cdot$

▶ The Octet Rule (page 188)

6. What is the octet rule? In forming compounds, atoms tend to achieve the electron configuration of a noble gas, which (except for helium) has eight electrons in its highest energy level.

7. Metallic atoms tend to lose their valence electrons to produce a(n) ___cation___ , or a positively charged ion. Most nonmetallic atoms achieve a complete octet by gaining or ___sharing___ electrons.

CHAPTER 7, Ionic and Metallic Bonding *(continued)*

▶ Formation of Cations (pages 188–190)

8. Write the electron configurations for these metals and circle the electrons lost when each metal forms a cation.

   a. Mg $\underline{\quad 1s^2 2s^2 2p^6 \; \boxed{2s^2} \quad}$

   b. Al $\underline{\quad 1s^2 2s^2 2p^6 \; \boxed{3s^2 3p^1} \quad}$

   c. K $\underline{\quad 1s^2 2s^2 2p^6 3s^2 3p^6 \; \boxed{4s^1} \quad}$

Match the noble gas with its electron configuration.

__c__	9. argon	a. $1s^2$
__a__	10. helium	b. $1s^2 2s^2 2p^6$
__b__	11. neon	c. $1s^2 2s^2 2p^6 3s^2 3p^6$
__d__	12. krypton	d. $1s^2 2s^2 2p^6 3s^2 3p^6 3d^{10} 4s^2 4p^6$

13. What is the electron configuration called that has 18 electrons in the outer energy level and all of the orbitals filled?

    pseudo noble-gas configuration

14. Write the electron configuration for zinc.

    $1s^2 2s^2 2p^6 3s^2 3p^6 3d^{10} 4s^2$

15. Fill in the electron configuration diagram for the copper(I) ion.

Copper atom
Cu

Copper(I) ion
Cu⁺

▶ Formation of Anions (pages 191–192)

16. Atoms of most nonmetallic elements achieve noble-gas electron configurations by gaining electrons to become ____anions____ , or negatively charged ions.

17. What property of nonmetallic elements makes them more likely to gain electrons than lose electrons?

    They have relatively full valence shells.

Name _____ Date _____ Class _____

18. Is the following sentence true or false? Elements of the halogen family lose one electron to become halide ions. _____false_____

19. How many electrons will each element gain in forming an ion?

    a. nitrogen ____3____

    b. oxygen ____2____

    c. sulfur ____2____

    d. bromine ____1____

20. Write the symbol and electron configuration for each ion from Question 19, and name the noble gas with the same configuration.

    a. nitride _____ N^{3-}; $1s^2 2s^2 2p^6$; neon _____

    b. oxide _____ O^{2-}; $1s^2 2s^2 2p^6$; neon _____

    c. sulfide _____ S^{2-}; $1s^2 2s^2 2p^6 3s^2 3p^6$; argon _____

    d. bromide _____ Br^-; $1s^2 2s^2 2p^6 3s^2 3p^6 3d^{10} 4s^2 4p^6$; krypton _____

SECTION 7.2 IONIC BONDS AND IONIC COMPOUNDS
(pages 194–199)

This section lists the characteristics of an ionic bond. It also describes the use of these characteristics to explain the electrical conductivity of ionic compounds when melted and when in aqueous solutions.

▶ Formation of Ionic Compounds (pages 194–195)

    1. What is an ionic bond? It is the electrostatic force of attraction that binds oppositely charged ions.

    2. In an ionic compound, the charges of the _____cations_____ and _____anions_____ must balance to produce an electrically _____neutral_____ substance.

    3. Complete the electron dot structures below to show how beryllium fluoride (BeF_2) is formed. Use figure on page 194 as a model.

CHAPTER 7, Ionic and Metallic Bonding *(continued)*

4. Why do beryllium and fluorine combine in a 1 : 2 ratio?

They combine in a 1 : 2 ratio because each beryllium atom gives up two electrons, but

each fluorine atom only accepts one electron. Therefore, two fluorine atoms are

needed to react with each beryllium atom.

5. A chemical formula shows the types and _____numbers_____ of atoms in the smallest representative unit of a substance.

6. List the numbers and types of atoms represented by these chemical formulas.

a. Fe_2O_3 _____2 atoms of iron, 3 atoms of oxygen_____

b. $KMnO_4$ _____1 atom of potassium, 1 atom of manganese, 4 atoms of oxygen_____

c. CH_3 _____1 atom of carbon, 4 atoms of hydrogen_____

d. NH_4NO_3 _____2 atoms of nitrogen, 4 atoms of hydrogen, 3 atoms of oxygen_____

7. What is a formula unit?

A formula unit is the lowest whole-number ratio of ions in an ionic compound.

8. Explain why the ratio of magnesium ions to chloride ions in $MgCl_2$ is 1 : 2.

There must be twice as many chloride ions (Cl^-) to balance the magnesium

ions (Mg^{2+}) to form an electrically neutral compound.

9. Describe the structure of ionic compounds.

Ionic compounds exist as collections of positively and negatively charged ions

arranged in repeating three-dimensional patterns.

▶ Properties of Ionic Compounds (pages 196–198)

10. Most ionic compounds are _____crystalline solids_____ at room temperature.

11. Is the following sentence true or false? Ionic compounds generally have low melting points. _____false_____

12. What does a coordination number tell you?

It is the number of ions of opposite charge that surround an ion in a crystal.

13. What is the coordination number of the ions in a crystal of NaCl? _____6_____

14. Circle the letter of each statement that is true about ionic compounds.

    a. When dissolved in water, ionic compounds can conduct electricity.

    b. When melted, ionic compounds do not conduct electricity.

    c. Ionic compounds have very unstable structures.

    d. Ionic compounds are electrically neutral.

Reading Skill Practice

By looking carefully at photographs and drawings in textbooks, you can better understand what you have read. Look carefully at Figure 7.9 on page 197. What important idea does this drawing communicate? Do your work on a separate sheet of paper.

The shape of a crystalline solid depends on the composition of the ionic compound that forms the crystal. Different combinations of ions produce different repeating three-dimensional patterns.

SECTION 7.3 BONDING IN METALS (pages 201–203)

This section uses the theory of metallic bonds to explain the physical properties of metals. It also describes the arrangements of atoms in some common metallic crystal structures.

▶ Metallic Bonds and Metallic Properties (pages 201–202)

1. Is the following sentence true or false? Metals are made up of cations, not neutral atoms. _____true_____

2. What are metallic bonds? Metallic bonds are the forces of attraction between free-floating valence electrons and positively charged metal ions.

3. Name three properties of metals that can be explained by metallic bonding.

    a. _____electrical conductivity_____

    b. _____ductility_____

    c. _____malleability_____

4. What happens to an ionic crystal when a force is applied to it?

The force tends to push ions of like charge into contact. They repel each other and the crystal shatters.

▶ Crystalline Structure of Metals (page 202)

5. Metal atoms in crystals are arranged into very _____compact_____ and orderly patterns.

CHAPTER 7, Ionic and Metallic Bonding *(continued)*

6. Label each of the following arrangements of atoms with the correct name.

_____ body-centered cubic _____

_____ hexagonal close-packed _____

_____ face-centered cubic _____

7. Circle the letter of each metal whose atoms form a face-centered cubic pattern.

    a. magnesium   **c.** sodium

    (b.) copper   **(d.)** aluminum

Match the arrangement with the number of neighbors each atom in the arrangement has.

  _b_   **8.** body-centered cubic   **a.** 12

  _a_   **9.** face-centered cubic   **b.** 8

  _a_ **10.** hexagonal close-packed

▶ Alloys (page 203)

11. A mixture of two or more elements, at least one of which is a metal, is called a(n) _____alloy_____ .

12. Is the following sentence true or false? Pure metals are usually harder and more durable than alloys. _____false_____

13. The most common use of nonferrous alloys is in _____coins_____ .

14. What four properties make steel an important alloy?

    a. _____corrosion resistance_____

    b. _____ductility_____

    c. _____hardness_____

    d. _____toughness_____

15. What are the component elements for the following alloys?

    a. sterling silver   _____silver and copper_____

    b. brass   _____copper and zinc_____

    c. surgical steel   _____iron, chromium, nickel, and molybdenum_____

    d. cast iron   _____iron and carbon_____

16. _____Interstitial_____ alloys have smaller atoms that fit into the spaces between larger atoms. _____Substitutional_____ alloys have component atoms that are roughly equal in size.

Name _____ Date _____ Class _____

CHAPTER 7, Ionic and Metallic Bonding *(continued)*

GUIDED PRACTICE PROBLEM

GUIDED PRACTICE PROBLEM 12 *(page 196)*

12. Use electron dot structures to determine formulas of the ionic compounds formed when
    a. potassium reacts with iodine.
    b. aluminum reacts with oxygen.

a. potassium reacts with iodine.

Analyze

Step 1. Is one of the elements a metal? If so, which one? _____yes; potassium_____

Step 2. Metal atoms ___lose___ their valence electrons when forming ionic compounds.

Nonmetal atoms ___gain___ electrons when forming ionic compounds.

Solve

Step 3. Write the electron dot structures for the two atoms

potassium _____K•_____   iodine __________

Step 4. The metal atom, ___potassium___ , must lose ___1___ electron(s) in order

to achieve an octet in the next-lowest energy level. The nonmetal atom, ___iodine___ ,

must gain ___1___ electron(s) in order to achieve a complete octet.

Step 5. Using electron dot structures, write an equation that shows the formation of the ionic compound from the two elements. Make sure that the electrons lost equals the electrons gained.

$$K• + \; :\overset{..}{\underset{..}{I}}• \; \rightarrow \; K^+ \; :\overset{..}{\underset{..}{I}}:^-$$

Step 6. The chemical formula for the ionic compound formed is _____KI_____ .

b. aluminum reacts with oxygen.

Analyze

Step 1. Is one of the elements a metal? If so, which one? _____yes; aluminum_____

Step 2. Metal atoms ___lose___ their valence electrons when forming ionic compounds. Nonmetal atoms ___gain___ electrons when forming ionic compounds.

Solve

Step 3. Write the electron dot structures for the two atoms

aluminum $\cdot\dot{Al}\cdot$ _____   oxygen $\vcenter{\hbox{:}}\dot{O}\cdot$ _____

Step 4. The metal atom, ___aluminum___ , must lose ___3___ electron(s) in order to achieve an octet in the next-lowest energy level. The nonmetal atom, ___oxygen___ , must gain ___2___ electron(s) in order to achieve a complete octet.

Step 5. Using electron dot structures, write an equation that shows the formation of the ionic compound from the two elements. Make sure that the electrons lost equals the electrons gained.

Step 6. The chemical formula for the ionic compound formed is ___Al_2O_3___ .

8 COVALENT BONDING

SECTION 8.1 MOLECULAR COMPOUNDS (pages 213–216)

This section explains how to distinguish between ionic and molecular compounds.

▶ Molecules and Molecular Compounds (pages 213–214)

1. What is a covalent bond?

   A covalent bond is a bond formed when two atoms share electrons.

2. Most elements found in nature, with the exception of the ___noble gases___ , exist as molecules.

3. What is a molecule?

   A molecule is a neutral group of atoms joined together by covalent bonds.

   _____

4. Compounds that are formed when two or more atoms combine to form molecules are called ___molecular compounds___ .

5. Circle the letter of the substances that do NOT exist as molecules in nature.

   a. oxygen

   b. water

   c. neon

   d. ozone

   e. helium

6. List two properties of molecular compounds.

   a. low melting and boiling points

   b. exist as gases or liquids at room temperature

CHAPTER 8, Covalent Bonding *(continued)*

▶ Molecular Formulas (pages 215–216)

7. What is a molecular formula?

A molecular formula shows the types and numbers of atoms present in a molecule

of a compound.

Match each compound with its molecular formula.

___b___ **8.** carbon dioxide   **a.** C_2H_6

___a___ **9.** ethane   **b.** CO_2

___c___ **10.** ammonia   **c.** NH_3

11. Is the following sentence true or false? A molecular formula shows the arrangement of the atoms in a molecule. _____false_____

In the diagram, match the type of model or formula with its representation.

a. ball-and-stick model   **d.** space-filling molecular model

b. molecular formula   **e.** structural formula

c. perspective drawing

$NH_3(g)$

12. _____b_____

13. _____a_____

14. _____d_____

15. _____c_____

16. _____e_____

17. What is the arrangement of atoms within a molecule called?

_____molecular structure_____

Name _____ Date _____ Class _____

SECTION 8.2 THE NATURE OF COVALENT BONDING (pages 217–220)

This section uses electron dot structures to show the formation of single, double, and triple covalent bonds. It also describes and gives examples of coordinate covalent bonding, resonance structures, and exceptions to the octet rule.

▶ The Octet Rule in Covalent Bonding (page 217)

1. How does electron sharing occur in forming covalent bonds?

   Sharing of electrons usually occurs so that atoms acquire the electron configurations

   of noble gases.

▶ Single Covalent Bonds (pages 217–220)

2. Is the following sentence true or false? A shared pair of electrons is represented

   by a double dash. _____ false _____

3. Structural formulas show the arrangement of _____ atoms _____
   in molecules.

4. Use the electron dot diagram below. Circle each unshared pair of electrons in a
   water molecule.

5. Complete the electron dot structure for each molecule. Each molecule
   contains only single covalent bonds.

   a. NH_3 **b.** H_2O_2 **c.** CH_4

▶ Double and Triple Covalent Bonds (pages 221–222)

6. A chemical bond formed when atoms share two pairs of electrons is called a(n)

   _____ double covalent bond _____ .

7. How many covalent bonds are in the nitrogen molecule?

   _____ three _____

CHAPTER 8, Covalent Bonding *(continued)*

8. Is the following sentence true or false? All diatomic molecules contain double

bonds. _____ false _____

▶ Coordinate Covalent Bonds (pages 223–225)

9. What is a coordinate covalent bond?

It is a covalent bond in which one atom contributes both bonding electrons.

10. Look at Table 8.2 on page 224. Which two nitrogen compounds contain
coordinate covalent bonds?

nitrogen dioxide and nitrous oxide

11. Complete the electron dot formula of the chlorate ion (ClO_3^-) by filling in the
bonds and unpaired electrons.

▶ Bond Dissociation Energies (page 226)

12. What is bond dissociation energy?

Bond dissociation energy is the energy required to break the bond between two

covalently bonded atoms.

13. Is the following sentence true or false? Molecules with high bond dissociation

energies are relatively unreactive. _____ true _____

14. What is the bond energy for covalent bond C — O?

347 kJ/mol

▶ **Resonance** (pages 227–228)

15. The actual bonding in ozone is a _____ hybrid _____ of the extremes represented by its _____ resonance structures _____ .

16. What are resonance structures?

They are structures that occur when it is possible to write two or more valid electron

dot formulas that have the same number of electron pairs for a molecule or ion.

▶ **Exceptions to the Octet Rule** (pages 228–229)

17. Why does NO_2 not follow the octet rule?

There is an unpaired electron present in both possible resonance structures.

SECTION 8.3 BONDING THEORIES (pages 230–236)

This section describes the molecular orbital theory of covalent bonding, including orbital hybridization. It also explains the use of VSEPR theory to predict the shapes of some molecules.

▶ **Molecular Orbitals** (pages 230–231)

1. What is a molecular orbital?

When two atoms combine, their atomic orbitals overlap to produce orbitals that apply

to the entire molecule.

2. Is the following sentence true or false? Electrons fill the antibonding molecular orbital first to produce a stable covalent bond. _____ false _____

3. When two *s* atomic orbitals combine, the molecular orbital formed is called a(n) _____ sigma _____ bond.

4. Circle the letter of each type of covalent bond that can be formed when *p* atomic orbitals overlap.

(a.) pi   **b.** beta   (c.) sigma   **d.** alpha

▶ **VSEPR Theory** (pages 232–233)

5. What is VSEPR theory?

The valence-shell electron-pair repulsion theory states that because electron pairs repel,

molecular shape adjusts so the valence-electron pairs are as far apart as possible.

6. When the central atom of a molecule has unshared electrons, the bond angles will be _____ smaller _____ than when all the central atom's electrons are shared.

CHAPTER 8, Covalent Bonding *(continued)*

7. What is the bond angle in carbon dioxide? Why?

The bond angle is 180° because the carbon atom has no unshared electron pairs.

8. What are the names of these common molecular shapes?

Linear triatomic   Pyramidal   Bent triatomic

Trigonal planar   Tetrahedral   Trigonal bipyramidal

▶ Hybrid Orbitals (pages 234–236)

9. Is the following sentence true or false? Orbital hybridization theory can describe both the shape and bonding of molecules. _____true_____

10. What is orbital hybridization?

Orbital hybridization occurs when several atomic orbitals mix to form the same total

number of equivalent hybrid orbitals.

Match the hybrid orbitals formed by carbon with the carbon compound in which they are found.

___c___ **11.** sp^3 **a.** ethyne

___b___ **12.** sp^2 **b.** ethene

___a___ **13.** sp **c.** methane

Reading Skill Practice

You can increase your understanding of what you have read by making comparisons. A compare/contrast table can help you do this. On a separate sheet of paper, draw a table to compare the three types of hybrid orbitals as explained on pages 235 and 236. The three heads for the rows should be *sp, sp²*, and *sp³*. Then list the characteristics that will form the basis of your comparison above each column. The column heads should be *Number of Hybrid Orbitals, Component Orbitals, Number of Bonds*, and *Bond Angle*.

Students' tables should include the basic information about the three types of hybrid orbitals contained on pages 235–236.

SECTION 8.4 POLAR BONDS AND MOLECULES (pages 237–244)

This section explains the use of electronegativity values to classify a bond as nonpolar covalent, polar covalent, or ionic. It also names and describes the weak attractive forces that hold groups of molecules together.

▶ Bond Polarity (pages 237–238)

1. Is the following statement true or false? Covalent bonds differ in the way electrons are shared by the bonded atoms, depending on the kind and number of atoms joined together. _____true_____

2. Describe how electrons are shared in each type of bond. Write *equally* or *unequally*.

   a. Nonpolar bond _____equally_____   **b.** Polar bond _____unequally_____

3. Why does the chlorine atom in hydrogen chloride acquire a slightly negative charge? Chlorine has a higher electronegativity than hydrogen, and, therefore, attracts the bonding electrons slightly away from hydrogen.

4. What symbols are used to represent the charges on atoms in a polar covalent bond? The polarity of the bond? _____$\delta+$ or $\delta-$; $+\!\longrightarrow$_____

Match the electronegativity difference range with the most probable type of bond that will form.

b	**5.** 0.0–0.4	**a.** ionic
d	**6.** 0.4–1.0	**b.** nonpolar covalent
c	**7.** 1.0–2.0	**c.** very polar covalent
a	**8.** > 2.0	**d.** moderately polar covalent

CHAPTER 8, Covalent Bonding *(continued)*

▶ Polar Molecules (pages 239–240)

9. Circle the letter of each sentence that is true about polar molecules.

   (a.) Some regions of a polar molecule are slightly negative and some are slightly positive.

   b. A molecule containing a polar bond is always polar.

   (c.) A molecule that has two poles is called a dipolar molecule.

   (d.) When polar molecules are placed in an electric field, they all line up with the same orientation in relation to the charged plates.

10. Are the following molecules polar or nonpolar?

   a. H_2O _____ polar _____   c. NH_3 _____ polar _____

   b. CO_2 _____ nonpolar _____   d. HCl _____ polar _____

▶ Attractions Between Molecules (pages 240–241)

11. What causes dispersion?

   Dispersion forces are caused by the motion of electrons.

   _____

12. Is the following sentence true or false? Dispersion forces generally increase in strength as the number of electrons in a molecule increases. _____ true _____

13. The strongest of the intermolecular forces are _____ hydrogen bonds _____ .

▶ Intermolecular Attractions and Molecular Properties (pages 243–244)

14. What determines the physical properties of a compound?

   The physical properties depend on the type of bonding in the compound.

15. Use Table 8.4 on page 244. Complete the following table comparing ionic and covalent compounds.

Characteristic	Ionic Compound	Covalent Compound
Representative unit	formula unit	molecule
Physical state	solid	solid, liquid, or gas
Melting point	high	low
Solubility in water	usually high	high to low

GUIDED PRACTICE PROBLEM

GUIDED PRACTICE PROBLEM 19 (page 239)

19. Identify the bonds between atoms of each pair of elements as nonpolar covalent, moderately polar covalent, very polar covalent, or ionic.

a. H and Br   **b.** K and Cl   **c.** C and O   **d.** Br and Br

Analyze

Step 1. What is the most probable type of bond for each electronegativity difference range?

Electronegativity Difference Range	Most Probable Type of Bond
0.0–0.4	nonpolar covalent
0.4–1.0	moderately polar covalent
1.0–2.0	very polar covalent
≥ 2.0	ionic

Calculate

Step 2. From Table 6.2 on page 177, determine the electronegativity values and differences for each pair of elements.

a. H = 2.1, Br = $\boxed{2.8}$; difference = $\boxed{0.7}$

b. K = $\boxed{0.8}$, Cl = 3.0; difference = $\boxed{2.2}$

c. C = $\boxed{2.5}$, O = 3.5; difference = $\boxed{1}$

d. Br = 2.8, Br = $\boxed{2.8}$; difference = $\boxed{0}$

Step 3. Refer to Table 8.3 on page 238 to determine the most probable type of bond for each compound.

a. moderately polar covalent

b. ionic

c. very polar covalent

d. nonpolar covalent

Evaluate

Step 4. How do you know that your answers are correct?

The answers are consistent with the magnitudes of the electronegativity differences.

CHEMICAL NAMES AND FORMULAS

SECTION 9.1 NAMING IONS (pages 253–258)

This section explains the use of the periodic table to determine the charge of an ion. It also defines polyatomic ion *and gives the names and formulas for the most common polyatomic ions.*

▶ Monatomic Ions (pages 253–256)

1. What are monatomic ions?

   Monatomic ions are ions consisting of only one atom.

2. How is the ionic charge of a Group 1A, 2A, or 3A ion determined?

   The ionic charge is numerically equal to the group number.

3. How is the ionic charge of a Group 5A, 6A, or 7A ion determined?

   The charge of an ion in Groups 5A, 6A, or 7A is determined by subtracting 8 from

   the group number.

4. Circle the letter of the type of element that often has more than one common ionic charge.

   a. alkali metal

   b. alkaline earth metal

   c. transition metal

   d. nonmetal

5. The _____Stock system_____ of naming transition metal cations uses a Roman numeral in parentheses to indicate the numeric value of the ionic charge.

6. An older naming system uses the suffix *-ous* to name the cation with the

   _____lesser_____ charge, and the suffix *-ic* to name the cation with the

   _____greater_____ charge.

7. What is a major advantage of the Stock system over the old naming system?

   The Stock system gives the actual charge of the ion.

CHAPTER 9, Chemical Names and Formulas *(continued)*

8. Use the periodic table to write the name and formula (including charge) for each ion in the table below.

Element	Name	Formula
Fluorine	fluoride ion	F^-
Calcium	calcium ion	Ca^{2+}
Oxygen	oxide ion	O^{2-}

▶ Polyatomic Ions (pages 257–258)

9. What is a polyatomic ion?

A polyatomic ion is a tightly bound group of atoms that behaves as a unit and carries a charge.

10. Is the following sentence true or false? The names of polyatomic anions always end in *-ide*. _____ false _____

11. What is the difference between the anions sulfite and sulfate?

The sulfite ion has one less oxygen atom than the sulfate ion.

12. Look at Table 9.3 on page 257. Circle the letter of a polyatomic ion that is a cation.

(**a.**) ammonium

b. acetate

c. oxalate

d. phosphate

13. How many atoms make up the oxalate ion and what is its charge?

It is made up of 6 atoms (2 carbon atoms and 4 oxygen atoms) and it has a charge of $2-$.

14. What three hydrogen-containing polyatomic anions are essential components of living systems?

a. _____ hydrogen carbonate ion _____

b. _____ hydrogen phosphate ion _____

c. _____ dihydrogen phosphate ion _____

15. Look at Figure 9.5 on page 257. Identify each of the ions shown below.

a. _____ammonium ion_____ **b.** _____phosphate ion_____ **c.** _____nitrate ion_____

SECTION 9.2 NAMING AND WRITING FORMULAS FOR IONIC COMPOUNDS (pages 260–266)

This section explains the rules for naming and writing formulas for binary ionic compounds and compounds containing a polyatomic ion.

▶ Binary Ionic Compounds (pages 260–263)

1. Traditionally, common names were based on some _____property_____ of a compound or its _____source_____ .

2. What is the general name for compounds composed of two elements?
   _____They are binary compounds._____

3. When writing the formula for any ionic compound, the charges of the ions must _____balance_____ .

4. What are two methods for writing a balanced formula?
   a. _finding the least common multiple of the charges_
   b. _using the crisscross method_

5. What are the formulas for the compounds formed by the following pairs of ions?
   a. Fe^{2+}, Cl^- _____$FeCl_2$_____
   b. Cr^{3+}, O^{2-} _____Cr_2O_3_____
   c. Na^+, S^{2-} _____Na_2S_____

6. What are the formulas for these compounds?
   a. lithium bromide _____$LiBr$_____
   b. cupric nitride _____Cu_3N_2_____
   c. magnesium chloride _____$MgCl_2$_____

7. The name of a binary ionic compound is written with the name of the _____cation_____ first followed by the name of the _____anion_____ .

CHAPTER 9, Chemical Names and Formulas *(continued)*

8. How can you tell that cobalt(II) iodide is a binary ionic compound formed by a transition metal with more than one ionic charge?

   The name includes a Roman numeral representing the ionic charge of the transition

   metal cation.

9. Write the names for these binary ionic compounds.

   a. PbS _____ lead(II) sulfide _____

   b. $MgCl_2$ _____ magnesium chloride _____

   c. Al_2Se_3 _____ aluminum selenide _____

▶ Compounds with Polyatomic Ions *(pages 264–266)*

10. What is a polyatomic ion?

    A polyatomic ion contains more than one element.

11. How do you write the formula for a compound containing a polyatomic ion?

    Write the symbol for the cation followed by the formula for the polyatomic ion

    and balance the charges.

12. Why are parentheses used to write the formula $Al(OH)_3$?

    The parentheses indicate how many polyatomic ions are needed in the formula.

13. Complete the table for these ionic compounds containing polyatomic ions.

Cation	Anion	Name	Formula
NH_4^+	S^{2-}	ammonium sulfide	$(NH_4)_2S$
Fe^{3+}	CO_3^{2-}	iron(III) carbonate	$Fe_2(CO_3)_3$
Ag^+	NO_3^-	silver nitrate	$AgNO_3$
K^+	CN^-	potassium cyanide	KCN

SECTION 9.3 NAMING AND WRITING FORMULAS FOR MOLECULAR COMPOUNDS (pages 268–270)

This section explains the rules for naming and writing formulas for binary molecular compounds.

▶ Naming Binary Molecular Compounds (pages 268–269)

1. Circle the letter of the type(s) of elements that form binary molecular compounds.

   a. two nonmetallic elements

   b. a metal and a nonmetal

   c. two metals

2. Is the following sentence true or false? Two nonmetallic elements can combine in only one way. _____false_____

3. What method is used to distinguish between different molecular compounds that contain the same elements? _____Prefixes are used._____

Match the prefix with the number it indicates.

___c___	**4.** *octa-*	**a.** 4
___a___	**5.** *tetra-*	**b.** 7
___b___	**6.** *hepta-*	**c.** 8
___d___	**7.** *nona-*	**d.** 9

8. What are the names of the following compounds?

   a. BF_3 _____boron trifluoride_____

   b. N_2O_4 _____dinitrogen tetroxide_____

   c. P_4S_7 _____tetraphosphorus heptasulfide_____

▶ Writing Formulas for Binary Molecular Compounds (page 270)

9. What are the formulas for the following compounds?

   a. carbon tetrabromide _____CBr_4_____

   b. nitrogen triiodide _____NI_3_____

   c. iodine monochloride _____ICl_____

   d. tetraiodine nonaoxide _____I_4O_9_____

CHAPTER 9, Chemical Names and Formulas *(continued)*

 # Reading Skill Practice

Writing a summary can help you remember the information you have read. When you write a summary, include only the most important points. Write a summary of the information in Section 9.3 on pages 268–269. Your summary should be shorter than the text on which it is based. Do your work on a separate sheet of paper.

Students' summaries should focus on the main points of each subsection and include the information given in Table 9.4.

SECTION 9.4 NAMING AND WRITING FORMULAS
FOR ACIDS AND BASES (pages 271–273)

This section explains the three rules for naming acids and shows how these rules can also be used to write the formulas for acids. Names and formulas for bases are also explained.

▶ **Naming Common Acids** (pages 271–272)

1. Acids produce _____hydrogen_____ ions when dissolved in water.

2. When naming acids, you can consider them to be combinations of
   _____anions_____ connected to as many _____hydrogen_____ ions
   as are necessary to create an electrically neutral compound.

3. What is the formula for hydrobromic acid? _____HBr_____

4. What are the components of phosphorous acid? What is its formula?
   hydrogen ion and phosphite ion; H_3PO_3

▶**Writing Formulas for Acids** (page 272)

5. Use Table 9.5 on page 272 to help you complete the table about acids.

Acid Name	Formula	Anion Name
acetic acid	$HC_2H_3O_2$	acetate
carbonic acid	H_2CO_3	carbonate
hydrochloric acid	HCl	chloride
nitric acid	HNO_3	nitrate
phosphoric acid	H_3PO_4	phosphate
sulfuric acid	H_2SO_4	sulfate

▶ **Names and Formulas for Bases (page 273)**

6. A base is a compound that produces _____hydroxide ions_____ when dissolved in water.

7. How are bases named?

Name the cation first followed by the anion (hydroxide ion).

SECTION 9.5 THE LAWS GOVERNING FORMULAS AND NAMES (pages 274–279)

This section uses data to demonstrate that a compound obeys the law of definite proportions. It also explains how to use flow charts to write the name and formula of a compound.

▶ **The Laws of Definite and Multiple Proportions (pages 274–275)**

1. What is the law of definite proportions?

In different samples of the same chemical compound, the masses of the elements

are always present in the same proportions.

2. Circle the whole-number mass ratio of Li to Cl in LiCl. The atomic mass of Li is 6.9; the atomic mass of Cl is 35.5.

a. 42 : 1

b. 5 : 1

c. 1 : 5

3. Circle the whole-number mass ratio of carbon to hydrogen in C_2H_4. The atomic mass of C is 12.0; the atomic mass of H is 1.0.

a. 1 : 6   **c.** 1 : 12

b. 6 : 1   **d.** 12 : 1

4. In the compound sulfur dioxide, a food preservative, the mass ratio of sulfur to oxygen is 1 : 1. An 80-g sample of a compound composed of sulfur and oxygen contains 48 g of oxygen. Is the sample sulfur dioxide? Explain.

No; If the sample contains 48 g of oxygen, it contains 32 g of sulfur. The ratio 32 : 48

is equivalent to 2 : 3, not 1 : 1.

5. What is the law of multiple proportions?

When two elements form more than one compound, the different masses of one

element that combine with the same mass of the other element are in a ratio of

small whole numbers.

CHAPTER 9, Chemical Names and Formulas *(continued)*

6. Complete the table using the law of multiple proportions.

	Mass of Cu	Mass of Cl	Mass Ratio Cl : Cu	Whole-number Ratio of Cl
Compound A	8.3 g	4.6 g	0.55	1
Compound B	3.3 g	3.6 g	1.1	2

▶ **Practicing Skills: Naming Chemical Compounds** (pages 276–277)

7. How can a flowchart help you to name chemical compounds?

It gives step-by-step directions for naming a compound.

8. Use the flowchart in Figure 9.20 on page 277 to write the names of the following compounds:

a. CsCl _____ cesium chloride _____

b. SnSe$_2$ _____ tin(IV) selenide _____

c. NH$_4$OH _____ ammonium hydroxide _____

d. HF _____ hydrofluoric acid _____

e. Si$_3$N$_4$ _____ trisilicon tetranitride _____

9. Complete the following five rules for writing a chemical formula from a chemical name.

a. In an ionic compound, the net ionic charge is _____ zero _____ .

b. An *-ide* ending generally indicates a _____ binary _____ compound.

c. An *-ite* or *-ate* ending means there is a _____ polyatomic _____ ion that includes oxygen in the formula.

d. _____ Prefixes _____ in a name generally indicate that the compound is molecular and show the number of each kind of atom in the molecule.

e. A _____ Roman numeral _____ after the name of a cation shows the ionic charge of the cation.

▶ Practicing Skills: Writing Chemical Formulas (page 278)

10. Fill in the missing labels from Figure 9.22 on page 278.

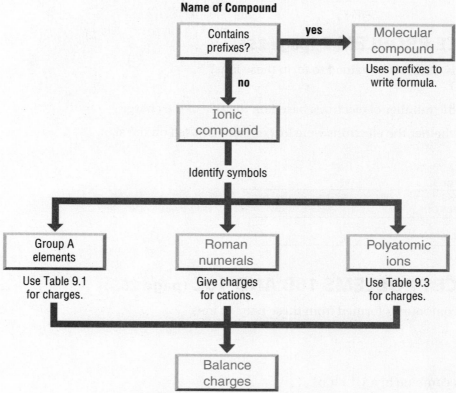

Name of Compound

Contains prefixes?

yes → Molecular compound
Uses prefixes to write formula.

no

Ionic compound

Identify symbols

Group A elements
Use Table 9.1 for charges.

Roman numerals
Give charges for cations.

Polyatomic ions
Use Table 9.3 for charges.

Balance charges
Use crisscross method. Add parentheses for any multiple polyatomic ions.

11. Use the flowchart in Figure 9.22 to write the formulas of the following compounds:

a. potassium silicate _____ K_2SiO_3

b. phosphorus pentachloride _____ PCl_5

c. manganese(II) chromate _____ $MnCrO_4$

d. lithium hydride _____ LiH

e. diiodine pentoxide _____ I_2O_5

CHAPTER 9, Chemical Names and Formulas *(continued)*

GUIDED PRACTICE PROBLEMS

GUIDED PRACTICE PROBLEM 2 (page 256)

2. How many electrons were lost or gained to form these ions?

   a. Fe^{3+} **b.** O^{2-} **c.** Cu^+

Step 1. Determine the number of electrons based on the size of the charge.

Step 2. Determine whether the electrons were lost or gained based on the sign of the charge.

   a. Fe^{3+} lost 3 electrons.

   b. O^{2-} gained 2 electrons.

   c. Cu^+ lost 1 electron.

GUIDED PRACTICE PROBLEMS 10B AND 10C (page 263)

10. Write formulas for compounds formed from these pairs of ions.

   b. Li^+, O^{2-}

Analyze

   Step 1. Do the ions combine in a 1:1 ratio?

   No, the charges on the ions are not equal.

Solve

   Step 2. Use the crisscross method to balance the formula.

   Write the formula. _____ Li_2O _____

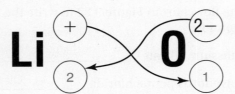

Evaluate

   Step 3. How do you know your formula is reasonable?

   The positive and negative charges are equal.

c. Ca^{2+}, N^{3-}

Analyze

Step 1. Will the calcium (Ca^{2+}) and nitride (N^{3-}) ions combine in a 1 : 1 ratio? How do you know?

No, because then the total charge would be negative, instead of neutral.

Solve

Step 2. Use the crisscross method to balance the formula.

Write the formula. _____ Ca_3N_2 _____

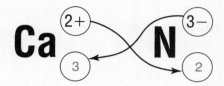

Evaluate

Step 3. How do you know this formula is reasonable?

The positive and negative charges are equal.

GUIDED PRACTICE PROBLEM 13B (page 265)

13b. Write the formula for chromium(III) nitrate.

- Is the compound ionic or molecular? Explain.

  It is ionic because it has no prefixes and it contains a metal.

- Use Table 9.3 on page 257 to write the formula for the nitrate ion. _____ NO_3^- _____

- Use the crisscross method to balance the formula.

- Write the formula. _____ $Cr(NO_3)_3$ _____

CHAPTER 9, Chemical Names and Formulas *(continued)*

GUIDED PRACTICE PROBLEM 34 (page 275)

34. Lead forms two compounds with oxygen. One compound contains 2.98 g of lead and 0.461 g of oxygen. The other contains 9.89 g of lead and 0.763 g of oxygen. For a given mass of oxygen, what is the lowest whole-number mass ratio of lead in the two compounds?

Complete the following steps to solve the problem.

	First compound	Second compound
Step 1. Write the ratio of lead to oxygen for each compound.	$\dfrac{2.98 \text{ g lead}}{0.461 \text{ g oxygen}}$	$\dfrac{9.89 \text{ g lead}}{0.763 \text{ g oxygen}}$
Step 2. Divide the numerator by the denominator in each ratio.	$\dfrac{6.46 \text{ g lead}}{\text{g oxygen}}$	$\dfrac{13.0 \text{ g lead}}{\text{g oxygen}}$
Step 3. Write a ratio comparing the first compound to the second.	$\dfrac{6.46 \text{ g lead/g oxygen}}{13.0 \text{ g lead/g oxygen}}$	
Step 4. Simplify. Note that this ratio has no units.	$\dfrac{0.497}{1} = \text{roughly } \dfrac{1}{2}$	

The mass ratio of lead per gram of oxygen in the two compounds is ____1 : 2____ .

10 CHEMICAL QUANTITIES

SECTION 10.1 THE MOLE: A MEASUREMENT OF MATTER (pages 287–296)

This section defines the mole and explains how the mole is used to measure matter. It also teaches you how to calculate the mass of a mole of any substance.

▶ Measuring Matter (pages 287–289)

1. What do the questions "how much?" and "how many?" have in common?

   They are questions about the amount of a substantce and are similar to questions

   scientists ask.

2. List two or three ways to measure matter.

   count the matter, measure the mass or weight, measure the volume

▶ What Is a Mole? (pages 290–293)

3. Circle the letter of the term that is an SI unit for measuring the amount of a substance.

   a. dozen   **b.** ounce   **c.** pair   **(d.)** mole

4. What is Avogadro's number?

   6.02×10^{23} representative particles of a substance

5. Circle the letter of the term that is NOT a representative particle of a substance.

   a. molecule   **b.** atom   **(c.)** grain   **d.** formula unit

6. List the representative particle for each of the following types of substances.

   a. molecular compounds _____ molecule _____

   b. ionic compounds _____ formula unit _____

   c. elements _____ atom _____

7. Is the following sentence true or false? To determine the number of representative particles in a compound, you count the molecules by viewing them under a microscope. _____ false _____

8. How can you determine the number of atoms in a mole of a molecular compound?

   Use the chemical formula to find the number of atoms in one molecule and multiply

   this number by Avogadro's number, the number of particles in one mole.

CHAPTER 10, Chemical Quantities *(continued)*

9. Complete the table about representative particles and moles.

Representative Particles and Moles			
	Representative Particle	Chemical Formula	Representative Particles in 1.00 mol
Atomic oxygen	Atom	O	6.02×10^{23}
Oxygen gas	Molecule	O_2	6.02×10^{23}
Sodium ion	Ion	Na^+	6.02×10^{23}
Sodium chloride	Formula unit	NaCl	6.02×10^{23}

▶ **The Mass of a Mole of an Element** (pages 293–294)

10. What is the atomic mass of an element?

The atomic mass of an element is the mass of a single atom in atomic mass units.

11. Circle the letter of the phrase that completes this sentence correctly.
The atomic masses of all elements

a. are the same.

b. are based on the mass of the carbon isotope C-12.

c. are based on the mass of a hydrogen atom.

▶ **The Mass of a Mole of a Compound** (pages 295–296)

12. How do you determine the mass of a mole of a compound?

The mass of a mole of a compound is determined by adding the atomic masses of

the atoms making up the molecule.

13. Complete the labels on the diagram below.

 = +

SO_3 =   1 S atom   +   3 O atoms

__80.1__ amu = 32.1 amu + __48.0__ amu

14. What is the molar mass of a compound?

It is the mass of 1 mol of that compound.

15. Is the following sentence true or false? Molar masses can be calculated directly from atomic masses expressed in grams. _____ true _____

SECTION 10.2 MOLE–MASS AND MOLE–VOLUME RELATIONSHIPS (pages 297–303)

This section explains how to use molar mass and molar volume to convert among measurements of mass, volume, and number of particles.

▶ The Mole–Mass Relationship (pages 297–299)

1. What is the molar mass of a substance?

It is the mass (in grams) of one mole of the substance.

2. What is the molar mass of KI (potassium iodide)?

39.1 g K + 126.9 g I = 166.0 g KI

▶ The Mole–Volume Relationship (pages 300–302)

3. Is the following sentence true or false? The volumes of one mole of different solid and liquid substances are the same. _____ false _____

4. Circle the letter of each term that can complete this sentence correctly. The volume of a gas varies with a change in

  a. temperature.   **c.** pressure.

  b. the size of the container.   **d.** the amount of light in the container.

5. Circle the letter of the temperature that is defined as standard temperature.

  a. 0 K   **c.** 0°C

  b. 100 K   **d.** 100°C

6. Is the following sentence true or false? Standard pressure is 101.3 kPa or 1 atmosphere (atm). _____ true _____

7. What is the molar volume of a gas at standard temperature and pressure (STP)? _____ 22.4 L _____

8. What units do you normally use to describe the density of a gas?

_____ grams per liter (g/L) _____

CHAPTER 10, Chemical Quantities *(continued)*

9. What is Avogadro's hypothesis?

Avogadro's hypothesis says that equal volumes of gases at the same temperature

and pressure contain equal numbers of particles.

10. Look at Figure 10.9 on page 300 to help you answer this question. Why is Avogadro's hypothesis reasonable?

As long as the gas particles are not tightly packed, there is a great deal of empty

space between them. A container can easily accommodate the same number of

relatively large or relatively small gas particles.

11. How many gas particles occupy a volume of 22.4 L at standard temperature and pressure? 6.02×10^{23} particles

▶ The Mole Road Map (page 303)

12. The figure below shows how to convert from one unit to another unit. Write the missing conversion factors below.

a. $\dfrac{1.00\ \text{mol}}{22.4\ \text{L}}$

b. $\dfrac{1.00\ \text{mol}}{6.02 \times 10^{23}\ \text{particles}}$

c. $\dfrac{6.02 \times 10^{23}\ \text{particles}}{1.00\ \text{mol}}$

d. $\dfrac{\text{molar mass}}{1.00\ \text{mol}}$

SECTION 10.3 PERCENT COMPOSITION AND CHEMICAL
FORMULAS (pages 305–312)

This section explains how to calculate percent composition from chemical formulas or experimental data, and how to derive empirical and molecular formulas.

▶ **Percent Composition of a Compound** (pages 305–308)

1. How do you express relative amounts of each element in a compound?

   Relative amounts are expressed by the percent composition or the percent by mass.

2. Circle the letter of the phrase that completes this sentence correctly. The number of percent values in the percent composition of a compound is

   a. half as many as there are different elements in the compound.

   (b.) as many as there are different elements in the compound.

   c. twice as many as there are different elements in the compound.

3. What is the formula for the percent by mass of an element in a compound?

   $$\% \text{ mass of element} = \frac{\text{grams of element}}{\text{grams of compound}} \times 100\%$$

4. In the diagram below, which compound has a greater percent composition of chromium? _____ potassium dichromate _____

   How much greater is this percent? _____ 8.6% _____

   Potassium chromate, K_2CrO_4 Potassium dichromate, $K_2Cr_2O_7$

5. To calculate the percent composition of a known compound, start with the chemical formula of the compound and calculate the _____ molar mass _____ , which gives the mass of one mole of the compound.

6. Is the following sentence true or false? You can use percent composition to calculate the number of grams of an element in a given amount of a compound. _____ true _____

CHAPTER 10, Chemical Quantities *(continued)*

7. How do you calculate the grams of an element in a specific amount of a compound?

Multiply the mass of the compound by a conversion factor that is based on the

percent composition.

▶ Empirical Formulas (pages 309–310)

8. An empirical formula of a compound gives the _____lowest_____ whole-number ratio of the atoms of the elements in a compound.

9. Is the following sentence true or false? The empirical formula of a compound is always the same as the molecular formula. _____false_____

10. Look at Figure 10.16 and Table 10.3. Name three compounds that have an empirical formula of CH.

ethyne, styrene, benzene

11. Fill in the labels on the diagram below.

SO_3 molecule   composed of   __1__ S atom   and   3 __O__ atoms

MICROSCOPIC INTERPRETATION

SO₃

MACROSCOPIC INTERPRETATION

1 mol SO_3 composed of   __6.02 × 10²³__ sulfur atoms

and

__3__ × (__6.02__ × 10²³) oxygen atoms

▶ Molecular Formulas (pages 311–312)

12. The molecular formula of a compound is either the same as its empirical

formula or a _____whole-number multiple_____ of it.

13. What do you need to know to calculate the molecular formula of a compound?

You need the empirical formula of the compound and its molar mass.

14. If you divide the molar mass of a compound by the empirical formula mass, what is the result?

The result is the number of empirical formula units in a molecule of the compound.

15. What factor would you use to convert the empirical formula of a compound to a molecular formula?

the number of empirical formula units in a molecule of the compound

---

 # Reading Skill Practice

By looking carefully at photographs and illustrations in textbooks, you can better understand what you have read. Look carefully at Figure 10.15 on page 309. What important idea does this illustration communicate?

This illustration shows that a chemical formula, in this example CO_2, can be understood on the microscopic level in terms of atoms or on the macroscopic level in terms of moles of atoms.

CHAPTER 10, Chemical Quantities *(continued)*

GUIDED PRACTICE PROBLEMS

GUIDED PRACTICE PROBLEM 1 (page 289)

1. If 0.20 bushels is 1 dozen apples and a dozen apples has a mass of 2.0 kg, what is the mass of 0.50 bushel of apples?

Analyze

Step 1. List the knowns and the unknown.

Knowns

number of bushels = 0.5 bushel

0.20 bushel = 1 dozen apples

1 dozen apples = 2.0 kg

Unknown

Mass of 0.5 bushel of apples = ? kg

Use dimensional analysis to convert the number of bushels to the mass of apples, by following this sequence of conversions:

Number of bushels → dozens of apples → mass of apples

Calculate

Step 2. Solve for the unknown.
The first conversion factor is:

$$\frac{1 \text{ dozen apples}}{0.20 \text{ bushel}}$$

The second conversion factor is:

$$\frac{2.0 \text{ kg apples}}{1 \text{ dozen apples}}$$

Multiplying the number of bushels by these two conversion factors gives the answer in kilograms.

$$\text{mass of apples} = 0.50 \cancel{\text{ bushels}} \times \frac{1 \cancel{\text{ dozen apples}}}{0.20 \cancel{\text{ bushel}}} \times \frac{2.0 \text{ kg apples}}{1 \cancel{\text{ dozen apples}}} = 5.0 \text{ kg apples}$$

The mass of 0.50 bushel of apples is _____.

Evaluate

Step 3. Does the result make sense?

Because a dozen apples is 2.0 kg and 0.5 bushels is more than two dozen but less

than three dozen, the mass should be more than 4 kg (2 dozen × 2.0 kg) and less

than 6 kg (3 dozen × 2.0 kg).

GUIDED PRACTICE PROBLEM 3 (page 291)

3. How many moles is 2.80×10^{24} atoms of silicon?

Step 1. List what you know.

2.80×10^{24} atoms of Si

$\boxed{6.02 \times 10^{23}}$ atoms in one mole

Step 2. Multiply the atoms of silicon by a mol/atoms conversion factor.

2.80×10^{24} atoms Si $\times \dfrac{1 \text{ mol}}{\boxed{6.02 \times 10^{23}} \text{ atoms Si}}$

Step 3. Divide.

$\boxed{4.65}$ mol

GUIDED PRACTICE PROBLEM 5 (page 292)

5. How many atoms are in 1.14 mol SO_3?

Analyze

Step 1. List the knowns and the unknown.

Knowns

number of moles = 1.14 mol SO_3

1 mol SO_3 = 6.02×10^{23} molecules SO_3

1 molecule SO_3 = 4 atoms (1 S atom and 3 O atoms)

Unknown

1.14 mol SO_3 = ? atoms

Calculate

Step 2. Solve for the unknown.
The first conversion factor is $\dfrac{6.02 \times 10^{23} \text{ molecules of water}}{1 \text{ mol water}}$

The second conversion factor is $\dfrac{4 \text{ atoms}}{1 \text{ molecule } SO_3}$.

Multiply moles of SO_3 by these conversion factors:

number of atoms = 1.14 ~~mol SO_3~~ $\times \dfrac{6.02 \times 10^{23} \text{ ~~molecules of SO_3~~}}{1 \text{ ~~mol SO_3~~}} \times \dfrac{4 \text{ atoms}}{1 \text{ ~~molecule SO_3~~}}$.

= $\underline{\quad 2.75 \times 10^{24} \text{ atoms} \quad}$

Evaluate

Step 3. Does the result make sense?

Because 4 atoms are in a molecule of SO_3 and there is a little more than one mole of

molecules, the answer should be more than 4 times Avogadro's number of atoms.

CHAPTER 10, Chemical Quantities *(continued)*

EXTRA PRACTICE (similar to Practice Problem 5, page 292)

4. How many molecules is 0.360 mol of water?

Analyze

Step 1. List the knowns and the unknown.
Knowns

Number of mols of water = 0.360 mol water

1 mol water = 6.02×10^{23} molecules water

Unknown

0.360 mol water =? molecules water

Calculate

Step 2. Solve for the unknown.
The conversion factor is $\dfrac{6.02 \times 10^{23} \text{ molecules of water}}{1 \text{ mol water}}$

Multiplying mols of water by this conversion factor will give the answer

molecules of water = 0.360 ~~mol water~~ $\times \dfrac{6.02 \times 10^{23} \text{ molecules of water}}{1 \text{ ~~mol water~~}}$

= ___2.17×10^{23} molecules of water___

Evaluate

Step 3. Does the result make sense?

Since the given number of mols of water is about one-third mol, the result should

be about one-third of Avogadro's number of molecules (1/3 × 6 = 2).

GUIDED PRACTICE PROBLEM 7 (page 296)

7. Find the molar mass of PCl_3.

Analyze

Step 1. List the knowns and the unknown.
Knowns

Molecular formula = PCl_3

1 molar mass P = 31.0 g P

1 molar mass Cl = 35.5 g Cl

Name _____ Date _____ Class _____

Unknown

molar mass PCl_3 = ? g

Calculate

Step 2. Solve for the unknown.
Convert moles of phosphorus and chlorine to grams of phosphorus and chlorine. Then add to get the results.

$$1 \; \cancel{\text{mol P}} \times \frac{31.0 \text{ g P}}{1 \; \cancel{\text{mol P}}} = 31.0 \text{ g P}$$

$$3 \; \cancel{\text{mol Cl}} \times \frac{35.5 \text{ g Cl}}{1 \; \cancel{\text{mol Cl}}} = 106.5 \text{ g Cl}$$

molar mass of PCl_3 = _____137.5 g_____

Evaluate

Step 3. Does the result make sense?

The answer is the sum of the molar mass of phosphorus and three times the molar

mass of chlorine, expressed to the tenths decimal place.

EXTRA PRACTICE (similar to Practice Problem 5, page 292)

5. How many atoms are there in 2.00 moles of SO_3?

$$2.00 \; \cancel{\text{mol}} \times \frac{6.02 \times 10^{23} \text{ molecules SO}_3}{\cancel{\text{mol}}} \times \frac{4 \text{ atoms}}{\text{molecule SO}_3} = 4.82 \times 10^{24} \text{ atoms}$$

EXTRA PRACTICE (similar to Practice Problem 7, page 296)

7. Find the molar mass of table salt (sodium chloride).

The formula for sodium chloride is NaCl.

molar mass NaCl = 1 mol Na + 1 mol Cl

$$= (1 \; \cancel{\text{mol Na}} \times \frac{23.0 \text{ g}}{1 \; \cancel{\text{mol Na}}}) + (1 \; \cancel{\text{mol Cl}} \times \frac{35.5 \text{ g}}{1 \; \cancel{\text{mol Cl}}})$$

$$= 23.0 \text{ g} + 35.5 \text{ g} = 58.5 \text{ g}$$

EXTRA PRACTICE (similar to Practice Problem 8, page 296)

8. What is the mass of 1 mole of ozone (O_3)?

$$1 \; \cancel{\text{mol}} \; O_3 \times \frac{48.0 \text{ g O}_3}{1 \; \cancel{\text{mol}} \; O_3} = 48.0 \text{ g O}_3$$

Name _____ Date _____ Class _____

GUIDED PRACTICE PROBLEM 16 (page 298)

16. Find the mass, in grams, of 4.52×10^{-3} mol $C_{20}H_{42}$.

Analyze

Step 1. List the known and the unknown.
Known

number of moles = 4.52×10^{-3} mol $C_{20}H_{42}$

Unknown

mass = ? g $C_{20}H_{42}$

Calculate

Step 2. Solve for the unknown.
Determine the molar mass of $C_{20}H_{42}$:

1 mol $C_{20}H_{42}$ = 20 × 12.0 g + 42 × 1.0 g = 282 g

Multiply the given number of moles by the conversion factor:

$$\text{mass} = 4.52 \times 10^{-3}\ \cancel{\text{mol } C_{20}H_{42}} \times \frac{282\ \text{g } C_{20}H_{42}}{1\ \cancel{\text{mol } C_{20}H_{42}}} = \underline{\qquad 1.27\ \text{g } C_{20}H_{42} \qquad}$$

Evaluate

Step 3. Does the result make sense?

The amount of substance is a little more than four-one thousandths of a mole, so

the mass should be only a small fraction of the molar mass.

EXTRA PRACTICE (similar to Practice Problem 17, page 298)

17. Calculate the mass, in grams, of 10 mol of sodium sulfate (Na_2SO_4).

10 × (2 mol Na + 1 mol S + 4 mol O)

$$= 10 \times (2\ \cancel{\text{mol Na}} \times \frac{23.0\ \text{g}}{\cancel{\text{mol Na}}} + 1\ \cancel{\text{mol S}} \times \frac{32.1\ \text{g}}{\cancel{\text{mol S}}} + 4\ \cancel{\text{mol O}} \times \frac{16.0\ \text{g}}{\cancel{\text{mol O}}})$$

$$= 10 \times (46.0\ \text{g} + 32.1\ \text{g} + 64.0\ \text{g})$$

$$= 10 \times (142.1\ \text{g}) = 1421\ \text{g}$$

Calculate the mass, in grams, of 10 mol of iron(II) hydroxide ($Fe(OH)_2$).

10 × (1 mol Fe + 2 mol O + 2 mol H)

$$= 10 \times (1\ \cancel{\text{mol Fe}} \times \frac{55.8\ \text{g}}{\cancel{\text{mol Fe}}} + 2\ \cancel{\text{mol O}} \times \frac{16.0\ \text{g}}{\cancel{\text{mol O}}} + 2\ \cancel{\text{mol H}} \times \frac{1.0\ \text{g}}{\cancel{\text{mol H}}})$$

$$= 10 \times (55.8\ \text{g} + 32.0\ \text{g} + 2.0\ \text{g})$$

$$= 10 \times 89.8\ \text{g} = 898\ \text{g}$$

GUIDED PRACTICE PROBLEM 18 (page 299)

18. Find the number of moles in 3.70×10^{-1} g of boron.

Analyze

Step 1. List the known and the unknown.
Known

mass = 3.70×10^{-1} g boron

Unknown

number of moles = ? mol boron

The unknown number of moles is calculated by converting the known mass to the number of moles using a conversion factor of mass → moles.

Calculate

Step 2. Solve for the unknown.
Determine the molar mass of boron: 1 mol B = 10.8 g B

Multiply the given mass by the conversion factor relating mass of boron to moles of boron:

$$\text{mass} = 3.70 \times 10^{-1} \, \cancel{\text{g B}} \times \frac{1 \, \text{mol B}}{10.8 \, \cancel{\text{g B}}}$$

$$= \underline{\quad 3.43 \times 10^{-2} \, \text{mol B} \quad}$$

Evaluate

Step 3. Does the result make sense?

Because the value of the conversion factor is about one-tenth, the numerical result

should be about one-tenth of the given number of grams.

GUIDED PRACTICE PROBLEM 20 (page 301)

20. What is the volume of these gases at STP?
a. 3.20×10^{-3} mol CO_2
b. 3.70 mol N_2

a. 3.20×10^{-3} mol CO_2
Analyze

Step 1. List the knowns and the unknown.
Knowns

number of moles = 3.20×10^{-3} mol CO_2

1 mol CO_2 = 22.4 L CO_2

CHAPTER 10, Chemical Quantities *(continued)*

Unknown

volume = ? L CO_2

To convert moles to liters, use the relationship 1 mol CO_2 = 22.4 L CO_2 (at STP).

Calculate

Step 2. Solve for the unknown.
Multiply the given number of moles of CO_2 by the conversion factor to give the result.

volume = 3.20×10^{-3} mol CO_2 $\times$ $\dfrac{22.4 \text{ L } CO_2}{1 \text{ mol } CO_2}$

= _____ 7.17×10^{-2} L CO_2 _____

Evaluate

Step 3. Does the result make sense?

Because a mole of gas occupies a volume of a little more than 20 liters, the result

should be a little larger than twenty times the given number of moles.

b. 3.70 mol N_2

Analyze

Step 1. List the knowns and the unknown.
Knowns

number of moles = 3.70 mol N_2

1 mol N_2 = 22.4 L N_2

Unknown

volume = ? L N_2

Use the relationship 1 mol N_2 = 22.4 L N_2 (at STP) to convert moles to liters.

Calculate

Step 2. Solve for the unknown.
Multiply the given number of moles of N_2 by the conversion factor to give the result.

volume = 3.70 mol N_2 $\times$ $\dfrac{22.4 \text{ L } N_2}{1 \text{ mol } N_2}$

= _____ 82.9 L N_2 _____

Evaluate

Step 3. Does the result make sense?

Because the number of moles is slightly less than four, the result should be close

to, but less than 88 L.

GUIDED PRACTICE PROBLEM 22 (page 302)

22. A gaseous compound composed of sulfur and oxygen, which is linked to the formation of acid rain, has a density of 3.58 g/L at STP. What is the molar mass of this gas?

Analyze

Step 1. List the knowns and the unknown.
Knowns

density = 3.58 g/L

1 mol (gas at STP) = 22.4 L

Unknown

molar mass = ? g

To convert density (g/L) to molar mass (g/mol), a conversion factor of L/mol is needed.

Calculate

Step 2. Solve for the unknown.
Multiply the density by the conversion factor relating liters and moles.

$$\text{molar mass} = \frac{3.58 \text{ g}}{1 \text{ L}} \times \frac{22.4 \text{ L}}{1 \text{ mol}}$$

$$= \underline{\qquad 80.2 \text{ g/mol} \qquad}$$

Evaluate

Step 3. Does the result make sense?

Multiplying approximately 4 grams/liter by approximately 20 liters/mole yields

about 80 grams/mole.

CHAPTER 10, Chemical Quantities *(continued)*

GUIDED PRACTICE PROBLEM 32 (page 306)

32. A compound is formed when 9.03 g Mg combines with 3.48 g N. What is the percent composition of this compound?

Analyze

Step 1. List the known and the unknowns.
Knowns

mass of Mg = 9.03 g Mg

mass of N = 3.48 g N

mass of compound = 9.03 g Mg + 3.48 g N = 12.51 g

Unknowns

percent Mg = ? %

percent N = ? %

The percent of an element in a compound is the mass of the element in the compound divided by the mass of the compound. To be expressed as a percentage, the ratio must be multiplied by 100%.

Calculate

Step 2. Solve for the unknown.

$$\text{percent Mg} = \frac{9.03 \text{ g Mg}}{12.51 \text{ g compound}} \times 100\% = \underline{\quad 72.2\% \text{ Mg} \quad}$$

$$\text{percent N} = \frac{3.48 \text{ g N}}{12.51 \text{ g compound}} \times 100\% = \underline{\quad 27.8\% \text{ N} \quad}$$

Evaluate

Step 3. Does the result make sense?

The percents of the elements of the compound add up to 100%.

72.2% + 27.8% = 100%

GUIDED PRACTICE PROBLEM 34 (page 307)

34. Calculate the percent composition of these compounds.
   a. ethane (C_2H_6)
   b. sodium bisulfate ($NaHSO_4$)

a. ethane (C_2H_6)
Analyze

Step 1. List the knowns and the unknowns.
Knowns

mass of C in one mole ethane = 2×12.0 g = 24.0 g

mass of H in one mole ethane = 6×1.0 g = 6.0g

molar mass of C_2H_6 = 24.0 g + 6.0 g = 30.0 g

Unknowns

percent C = ? %

percent H = ? %

Because no masses are given, the percent composition can be determined based on the molar mass of the substance. The percent of an element in a compound is the mass of the element in the compound divided by the mass of the compound. To express the ratio as a percent, the ratio is multiplied by 100%.

Calculate

Step 2. Solve for the unknown.

$$\text{percent C} = \frac{24.0 \text{ g C}}{30.0 \text{ g compound}} \times 100\% = \underline{\quad 80.0\% \text{ C} \quad}$$

$$\text{percent H} = \frac{6.0 \text{ g H}}{30.0 \text{ g compound}} \times 100\% = \underline{\quad 20.0\% \text{ H} \quad}$$

Evaluate

Step 3. Does the result make sense?

The percents of the elements of the compound add up to 100%.

80.0% + 20.0% = 100%

CHAPTER 10, Chemical Quantities *(continued)*

b. sodium bisulfate ($NaHSO_4$)

Analyze

Step 1. List the knowns and the unknowns.

Knowns

mass of Na in one mole sodium bisulfate = 1×23.0g = 23.0 g

mass of H in one mole sodium bisulfate = 1×1.0 g = 1.0 g

mass of S in one mole sodium bisulfate = 1×32.1 g = 32.1 g

mass of O in one mole sodium bisulfate = 4×16.0 g = 64.0 g

molar mass of $NaHSO_4$ = 23.0 g + 1.0 g + 32.1 g + 64.0 g = 120.1 g

Unknowns

percent Na = ? %

percent H = ? %

percent S = ? %

percent O = ? %

Because no masses are given, the percent composition can be determined based on the molar mass of the substance. The percent of an element in a compound is the mass of the element in the compound divided by the mass of the compound. To express the ratio as a percent, the ratio is multiplied by 100%.

Calculate

Step 2. Solve for the unknown.

$$\text{percent Na} = \frac{23.0 \text{ g Na}}{120.1 \text{ g compound}} \times 100\% = \underline{\quad 19.2\% \text{ Na} \quad}$$

$$\text{percent H} = \frac{1.0 \text{ g H}}{120.1 \text{ g compound}} \times 100\% = \underline{\quad 0.83\% \text{ H} \quad}$$

$$\text{percent S} = \frac{32.1 \text{ g S}}{120.1 \text{ g compound}} \times 100\% = \underline{\quad 26.7\% \text{ C} \quad}$$

$$\text{percent O} = \frac{64.0 \text{ g O}}{120.1 \text{ g compound}} \times 100\% = \underline{\quad 53.3\% \text{ O} \quad}$$

Evaluate

Step 3. Does the result make sense?

The percents of the elements of the compound add up to 100%.

19.2% + 0.83% + 26.7% + 53.3% = 100%

GUIDED PRACTICE PROBLEM 36 (page 310)

36. Calculate the empirical formula of each compound.
   a. 94.1% O, 5.9% H
   b. 67.6% Hg, 10.8% S, 21.6% O

a. 94.1% O, 5.9% H

Analyze

Step 1. List the knowns and the unknown.

Knowns

percent composition: 94.1% O, 5.9% H

molar mass O = 16.0 g/mol O

molar mass H = 1.0 g/mol H

Unknown

empirical formula = $H_?O_?$

Use the percent composition to convert to mass, recalling that percent means parts per hundred. Then use the molar mass to convert to number of moles. Finally, determine whole number ratios based on the number of moles of each element per 100 grams of compound.

Calculate

Step 2. Solve for the unknown.
One hundred grams of compound has 5.9 g H and 94.1 g O.
Multiply by conversion factors relating moles of the elements to grams.

$$5.9 \ \cancel{g\,H} \times \frac{1 \ \text{mol H}}{1.0 \ \cancel{g\,H}} = 5.9 \ \text{mol H}$$

$$94.1 \ \cancel{g\,O} \times \frac{1 \ \text{mol O}}{16.0 \ \cancel{g\,O}} = 5.88 \ \text{mol O}$$

So the mole ratio for 100 g of the compound is $H_{5.9}O_{5.9}$. But formulas must have whole number subscripts. Divide each molar quantity by the smaller number of moles. This will give 1 mol for the element with the smaller number of moles. In this case, the ratio is one-to-one and so the empirical formula is simply H_1O_1. However, a subscript of one is never written, so the answer is __HO__.

Evaluate

Step 3. Does the result make sense?

The subscripts are whole numbers and the percent composition of this empirical

formula equals the percent compostion given in the original problem.

CHAPTER 10, Chemical Quantities *(continued)*

b. 67.6% Hg, 10.8% S, 21.6% O

Analyze

Step 1. List the knowns and the unknown.

Knowns

percent composition: 67.6% Hg, 10.8% S, 21.6% O

molar mass Hg = 200.6 g/mol Hg

molar mass S = 32.1 g/mol S

molar mass O = 16.0 g/mol O

Unknown

empirical formula = $Hg_?S_?O_?$

Use the percent composition to convert to mass. Then use molar mass to convert to number of moles. Finally, determine whole number ratios based on the number of moles of each element per 100 grams of compound.

Calculate

Step 2. Solve for the unknown.
One hundred grams of compound has 67.6 g Hg, 10.8 g S, and 21.6 g O.
Multiply by a conversion factor relating moles to grams.

$$67.6 \text{ g Hg} \times \frac{1 \text{ mol Hg}}{200.6 \text{ g Hg}} = 0.337 \text{ mol Hg}$$

$$10.8 \text{ g S} \times \frac{1 \text{ mol S}}{32.1 \text{ g S}} = 0.336 \text{ mol S}$$

$$21.6 \text{ g O} \times \frac{1 \text{ mol O}}{16.0 \text{ g O}} = 1.35 \text{ mol O}$$

So the mole ratio for 100 g of the compound is $Hg_{0.34}S_{0.34}O_{1.35}$.
Divide each molar quantity by the smaller number of moles.

$$\frac{0.34 \text{ mol Hg}}{0.34} = 1 \text{ mol Hg}$$

$$\frac{0.34 \text{ mol S}}{0.34} = 1 \text{ mol S}$$

$$\frac{1.35 \text{ mol O}}{1.35} = 4 \text{ mol O}$$

The empirical formula is _____ $HgSO_4$ _____ .

Evaluate

Step 3. Does the result make sense?

The subscripts are whole numbers and the percent composition of this empirical

formula equals the percent composition given in the original problem.

GUIDED PRACTICE PROBLEM 38 (page 312)

38. Find the molecular formula of ethylene glycol, which is used as antifreeze. The molar mass is 62 g/mol and the empirical formula is CH_3O.

Analyze

Step 1. List the knowns and the unknown.

Knowns

molar mass = 62 g/mol

empirical formula = CH_3O

Unknown

molecular formula = $C_2H_?O_?$

Calculate

Step 2. Solve for the unknown.
First, calculate the empirical formula mass (efm):

$$1 \text{ mol C} \times \frac{12 \text{ g C}}{1 \text{ mol C}} = 12 \text{ g C}$$

$$3 \text{ mol H} \times \frac{1.0 \text{ g H}}{1 \text{ mol H}} = 3 \text{ g H}$$

$$1 \text{ mol O} \times \frac{16 \text{ g O}}{1 \text{ mol O}} = 16 \text{ g O}$$

So efm = 12g + 3 g + 16 g = 31 g.

Divide the molar mass by the empirical formula mass:
Molar mass/efm = 62 g/31 g = 2

Multiply subscripts in the empirical formula by this value.

The molecular formula is _____ $C_2H_6O_2$ _____ .

Evaluate

Step 3. Does the result make sense?

The molecular formula has the given molar mass, and can be reduced to the

empirical formula.

11 CHEMICAL REACTIONS

SECTION 11.1 DESCRIBING CHEMICAL REACTIONS (pages 321–329)

This section explains how to write equations describing chemical reactions using appropriate symbols. It also describes how to write balanced chemical equations when given the names or formulas of the reactants and products in a chemical reaction.

▶ Writing Chemical Equations (pages 321–323)

1. A chemical reaction occurs when one or more _____reactants_____ change into one or more new substances called _____products_____ .

2. The arrow in a reaction means _____yields, gives, or reacts to produce_____

_____ .

3. Is the following sentence true or false? When there are two or more reactants or products, they are separated by an arrow. _____false_____

4. Write a word equation that describes the following reactions.

   a. Acetylene reacts with oxygen to produce carbon dioxide and water.

   acetylene + oxygen ⟶ carbon dioxide + water

   b. When heated, mercury(II) oxide reacts to form mercury and oxygen.

   mercury(II) oxide ⟶ mercury + oxygen

5. What is a chemical equation?

   A chemical equation is a representation of a chemical reaction; the formulas of the react-

   ants (on the left) are connected by an arrow with formulas of the products (on the right).

6. A chemical reaction that shows only the formulas, but not the relative amounts of the reactants and products is a(n) _____skeleton equation_____ .

7. Identify the reactant(s) and product(s) in the chemical equation $Li + Br_2 \longrightarrow LiBr$.

   a. reactant(s) _____Li and Br_2_____

   b. product(s) _____$LiBr$_____

8. Circle the letter of each statement that is true about a catalyst.

   a. A catalyst is the new material produced as a result of a chemical reaction.

   (b.) A catalyst is not used up in a chemical reaction.

   c. A catalyst adds heat to a chemical reaction.

   (d.) A catalyst speeds up a chemical reaction.

CHAPTER 11, Chemical Reactions *(continued)*

9. Use the symbols in Table 11.1 on page 323 to write a skeleton equation for the following chemical reaction. Hydrochloric acid reacts with zinc to produce aqueous zinc(II) chloride and hydrogen gas.

$HCl(aq) + Zn(s) \longrightarrow ZnCl_2(aq) + H_2(g)$ _____

▶ Balancing Chemical Equations (pages 324–328)

10. What is the law of conservation of mass?

In any physical or chemical change, mass is neither created nor destroyed. _____

11. Complete the flowchart for balancing equations.

Determine the correct formulas and physical states for

the _____reactants_____ and _____products_____ .

Write a _____skeleton equation_____ with the formulas for the reactants on the left and the formulas for the products on the right of a yields sign ($\longrightarrow$).

Count the number of _____atoms_____ of each element in the reactants and in the products.

Balance the number of atoms of the elements on the two sides of the equation by placing _____coefficients_____ in front of formulas. Never try to balance an equation by changing the _____subscripts_____ in formulas.

Check each atom or polyatomic ion to be sure the equation is _____balanced_____ , and make sure that all coefficients are in the _____lowest_____ possible ratio.

12. Balance the following chemical equations.

a. ___2___ Na(*s*) + ___2___ H₂O(*l*) ⟶ ___2___ NaOH(*aq*) + H₂(*g*)

b. ___2___ AgNO₃(*aq*) + Zn(*s*) ⟶ Zn(NO₃)₂(*aq*) + ___2___ Ag(*s*)

SECTION 11.2 TYPES OF CHEMICAL REACTIONS (pages 330–339)

This section explains how to identify a reaction as a combination, decomposition, single-replacement, double-replacement, or combustion reaction. It also describes how to predict the products of each type of reaction.

▶ Classifying Reactions (page 330)

1. There are _____five_____ general types of chemical reactions.

2. Complete the diagram of a combination reaction. Which characteristic of this type of reaction is shown in the diagram?

Two reactants combine to form a single compound. _____

_____

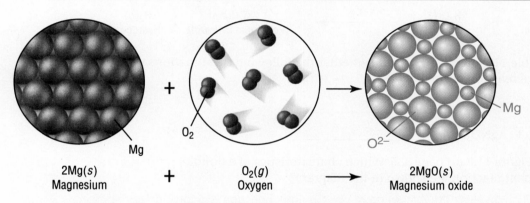

2Mg(*s*)   **+**   O₂(*g*)   ⟶   2MgO(*s*)
Magnesium   Oxygen   Magnesium oxide

3. Is the following sentence true or false? The product of a combination reaction is always a molecular compound. _____false_____

4. Circle the letter of each set of reactants that can produce more than one product.

  (**a.**) two nonmetals   (**c.**) a transition metal and a nonmetal

  b. a Group A metal and a nonmetal   **d.** two metals

5. Look at Figure 11.6 on page 332. Which characteristics of a decomposition reaction are shown in the diagram?

The reaction has a single reactant, which is a binary compound. The products are two

elements. _____

CHAPTER 11, Chemical Reactions *(continued)*

6. Rapid decomposition reactions can cause _____explosions_____ as a result of the formation of gaseous products and heat.

7. Most decomposition reactions require the addition of _____energy_____ in the form of heat, light, or electricity.

8. Complete the diagram of a single replacement reaction. Which characteristics of this type of reaction are shown in the diagram?

One element in a compound is replaced by another element.

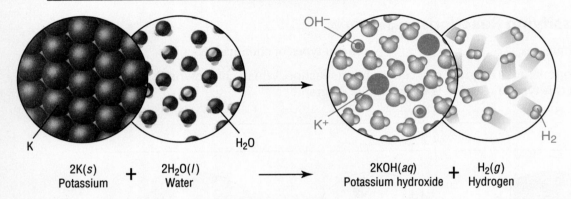

$2K(s)$	+	$2H_2O(l)$		$2KOH(aq)$	+	$H_2(g)$
Potassium		Water		Potassium hydroxide		Hydrogen

9. Using Table 11.2 on page 333, state whether the following combinations will produce a reaction or no reaction.

a. $Ag(s) + HCl(aq)$ _____no reaction_____

b. $Cu(s) + AgNO_3(aq)$ _____reaction_____

10. Look at Figure 11.8 on page 335. Which characteristics of a double-replacement reaction are shown in the diagram?

The reaction involves the exchange of positive ions between two ionic compounds in

an aqueous solution. One product precipitates from solution.

11. When solutions of ionic compounds are mixed, what three circumstances may indicate that a double-replacement reaction has occurred?

a. A precipitate forms.

b. A gas evolves.

c. One product is a molecular compound such as water.

12. Look at the diagram of a combustion reaction in Figure 11.9 on page 336. Which characteristics of this type of reaction are shown in the diagram?

One reactant is a compound and the other is oxygen.

13. Is the following sentence true or false? Hydrocarbons, compounds of hydrogen and carbon, are often the reactants in combustion reactions. _____true_____

14. Circle the letter of each compound that can be produced by combustion reactions.

    a. oxygen   **c.** water

    b. carbon dioxide   **d.** glucose

▶ Predicting the Products of a Chemical Reaction (pages 337–339)

15. Classify the reaction in each of the following equations.

    a. $BaCl_2(aq) + K_2CrO_4(aq) \longrightarrow BaCrO_4(s) + 2KCl\ (aq)$ _____double-replacement_____

    b. $Si(s) + 2Cl_2(g) \longrightarrow SiCl_4(l)$ _____combination_____

    c. $2C_6H_6(l) + 15O_2(g) \longrightarrow 6H_2O(l) + 12CO_2(g)$ _____combustion_____

16. Use Figure 11.10 on page 339. The equation for the combustion of pentane is $C_5H_{12} + 8O_2 \longrightarrow 5CO_2 + 6H_2O$. What numbers in this equation are represented by x and y in the general equation? _____5, 12_____

SECTION 11.3 REACTIONS IN AQUEOUS SOLUTION (pages 342–344)

This section explains how to write and balance net ionic equations. It also describes the use of solubility rules to predict the formation of precipitates in double-replacement reactions.

▶ Net Ionic Equations (pages 342–343)

1. Many important chemical reactions take place in _____aqueous solution_____ .

2. An equation that shows dissolved ionic compounds as their free ions is called a(n) _____complete ionic equation_____ .

3. Is the following sentence true or false? A spectator ion is not directly involved in a reaction. _____true_____

4. What is a net ionic equation? _A net ionic equation is an equation that shows only_ _those particles that actually take part in the reaction._

_____

CHAPTER 11, Chemical Reactions *(continued)*

5. Circle the letter of each sentence that is true about ionic equations.

    a. A complete ionic equation shows only the ions involved in the reaction.

    (b.) Spectator ions are left out of a net ionic equation.

    c. Atoms do not need to be balanced in an ionic equation.

    (d.) Ionic charges must be balanced in a net ionic equation.

6. Write the balanced net ionic equation for this reaction:
$Pb(NO_3)_2(aq) + KI(aq) \longrightarrow PbI_2(s) + KNO_3(aq)$. Show your work.

    Write the complete ionic equation:

    $Pb^{2+}(aq) + NO_3^-(aq) + K^+(aq) + I^-(aq) \longrightarrow PbI_2(s) + K^+(aq) + NO_3^-(aq)$

    eliminate the spectator ions: $Pb^{2+}(aq) + I^-(aq) \longrightarrow PbI_2(s)$

    balance the atoms and charges: $Pb^{2+}(aq) + 2I^-(aq) \longrightarrow PbI_2(s)$

▶ Predicting the Formation of a Precipitate (page 344)

7. What determines whether a precipitate forms when two solutions of ionic compounds are mixed?

    The solubilities of the new ionic compounds determine whether a precipitate will form.

8. Use Table 11.3 on page 344 to predict whether the following compounds are soluble or insoluble.

    a. $Fe(OH)_3$ _____ insoluble _____

    b. NaOH _____ soluble _____

    c. $Ca(ClO_3)_2$ _____ soluble _____

    d. $HgSO_4$ _____ insoluble _____

 # Reading Skill Practice

A flowchart can help you to remember the order in which events occur. On a separate sheet of paper, create a flowchart that describes the steps for writing a balanced net ionic equation. This process is explained on pages 342–343 of your textbook.

Students' flowcharts will vary. A typical flowchart might include these steps: Write a complete ionic equation that shows dissolved ionic compounds as their free ions. Eliminate the spectator ions from both sides of the equation. Balance the ionic charges in the net ionic equation. Balance the atoms on both sides of the equation.

GUIDED PRACTICE PROBLEMS

GUIDED PRACTICE PROBLEM 2 (page 324)

2. Sulfur burns in oxygen to form sulfur dioxide. Write a skeleton equation for this chemical reaction. Include appropriate symbols from table 11.1.

Analyze

Step 1. Identify the relevant concepts.
Write the formula for each reactant and each product. Include the common STP state of each substance.

Reactants

sulfur = $S(s)$

oxygen = $O_2(g)$

Products

sulfur dioxide = $SO_2(s)$

Solve

Step 2. Write the skeleton equation using + between reactants on the left hand side and → to separate reactants from products:

$S(s) + O_2(g) \rightarrow SO_2(s)$

GUIDED PRACTICE PROBLEM 3 (page 327)

3. Balance each equation.
   a. $AgNO_3 + H_2S \rightarrow Ag_2S + HNO_3$
   b. $Zn(OH)_2 + H_3PO_4 \rightarrow Zn_3(PO_4)_2 + H_2O$

a. $AgNO_3 + H_2S \rightarrow Ag_2S + HNO_3$

Analyze

Step 1. Identify the relevant concepts.
Count the number of atoms of each element on both sides of the skeleton equation.

Left hand side (lhs):	Right hand side (rhs):
1 Ag	2 Ag
1 N	1 N
1 S	1 S
2 H	1 H
3 O	3 O

CHAPTER 11, Chemical Reactions *(continued)*

Solve

Step 2. Apply concepts to this situation.
The reactant containing Ag on the lhs needs a multiple of 2, and the product containing H on the rhs needs a multiple of 2. Rewrite the equation with these coefficients and count again.

$$2AgNO_3 + H2S \rightarrow Ag_2S + 2HNO_3$$

Left hand side (lhs):   Right hand side (rhs):

2 Ag	2 Ag
2 N	2 N
1 S	1 S
2 H	2 H
6 O	6 O

Because the number of atoms of each element is the same on both sides, the

equation is balanced: _____ $2AgNO_3 + H_2S \rightarrow Ag_2S + 2HNO_3$ _____

b. $Zn(OH)_2 + H_3PO_4 \rightarrow Zn_3(PO_4)_2 + H_2O$

Analyze

Step 1. Look at the zinc ions on both sides of the equation. Make the number of zinc ions in zinc hydroxide match the number in zinc phosphate.

___3___ $Zn(OH)_2 + H_3PO_4 \longrightarrow Zn_3(PO_4)_2 + H_2O$

Step 2. Look at the phosphate ions on both sides of the equation. Make the number of phosphate ions in phosphoric acid match the number of phosphate ions in zinc phosphate.

$3Zn(OH)_2 + $ ___2___ $H_3PO_4 \longrightarrow Zn_3(PO_4)_2 + H_2O$

Step 3. Look at the remaining ions in the reactants—OH^- and H^+.

$3 \times$ ___2___ ions of OH^-
 _____ $\longrightarrow$ will form ___6___ molecules of H_2O
$2 \times$ ___3___ ions of H^+

Step 4. Complete the balanced equation.

___3___ $Zn(OH)_2 + $ ___2___ $H_3PO_4 \longrightarrow Zn_3(PO_4)_2 + $ ___6___ H_2O

GUIDED PRACTICE PROBLEM 5 (page 328)

5. Balance each equation.

   a. $FeCl_3 + NaOH \rightarrow Fe(OH)_3 + NaCl$

   b. $CS_2 + Cl_3 \rightarrow CCl_4 + S_2Cl_2$

a. $FeCl_3 + NaOH \rightarrow Fe(OH)_3 + NaCl$

Analyze

Step 1. Identify the relevant concepts.
Count the number of atoms of each element for both sides of the skeleton equation.

Solve

Step 2. Apply concepts to this situation.
The product containing Cl on the rhs needs a multiple of 3, which then means the reactant containing Na on the lhs needs a multiple of 3. Rewrite the equation with these coefficients and count again. This produces a balanced equation.

$FeCl_3 + 3NaOH \rightarrow Fe(OH)_3 + 3NaCl$

b. $CS_2 + Cl_3 \rightarrow CCl_4 + S_2Cl_2$

Analyze

Step 1. Identify the relevant concepts.
Count the number of atoms of each element for both sides of the skeleton equation.

Solve

Step 2. Apply concepts to this situation.
The product containing Cl on the lhs needs a multiple of 2 to give a total of six Cl atoms for the rhs. Rewrite the equation with these coefficients and count again. This produces a balanced equation.

$CS_2 + 2Cl_3 \rightarrow CCl_4 + S_2Cl_2$

GUIDED PRACTICE PROBLEM 13 (page 331)

13. Complete and balance the equation for a combination reaction.

    $Be + O_2 \rightarrow$

Analyze

Step 1. Identify the relevant concepts.
Beryllium is a group 2A metal, which means it will have a 1:1 bond with a group 6A gas, such as oxygen.

CHAPTER 11, Chemical Reactions *(continued)*

Solve

Step 2. Apply concepts to this situation.
The skeleton equation for this combination reaction is: $Be + O_2 \rightarrow BeO$

A coefficient of 2 is needed before the product to balance the number of oxygen atoms. Then a coefficient of 2 is needed before the reactant Be. The balanced equation is:

$2Be + O_2 \rightarrow 2BeO$

GUIDED PRACTICE PROBLEM 15 (page 332)

15. Complete and balance the equation for a decomposition reaction.
$HI \rightarrow$

Analyze

Step 1. Identify relevant concepts.
Remember that both hydrogen and iodine exist as diatomic molecules.

Solve

Step 2. Apply concepts to this situation.
The skeleton equation for this decomposition reaction is: $HI \rightarrow H_2 + I_2$

Balancing the equation gives the result.

$2HI \rightarrow H_2 + I_2$

GUIDED PRACTICE PROBLEM 17 (page 334)

17. Complete the equations for these single-replacement reactions in aqueous solution. Balance each equation. Write "no reaction" if a reaction does not occur. Use the activity series.
   a. $Fe(s) + Pb(NO_3)_2(aq) \rightarrow$
   b. $Cl_2(aq) + NaI(aq) \rightarrow$
   c. $Ca(s) + H_2O(l) \rightarrow$

a. $Fe(s) + Pb(NO_3)_2(aq) \rightarrow$

Analyze

Step 1. Identify relevant concepts.
Table 11.2 shows that iron is more reactive than lead.

Solve

Step 2. Apply concepts to this situation.
Fe replaces Pb. A reaction occurs resulting in the balanced equation:

$Fe(s) + Pb(NO_3)_2(aq) \rightarrow Pb(s) + Fe(NO_3)_2(aq)$

b. $Cl_2(aq) + NaI(aq) \rightarrow$

Analyze

Step 1. Identify relevant concepts.
On the periodic table, notice that Cl and I are group 7A halogens and Cl is more reactive than I.

Solve

Step 2. Apply concepts to this situation.
Cl replaces I. Recall that iodine exists as a diatomic molecule. A reaction occurs resulting in the skeleton equation:
$Cl_2(aq) + NaI(aq) \rightarrow I_2(aq) + NaCl(aq)$.

Balancing this equation gives this result.

$Cl_2(aq) + 2NaI(aq) \rightarrow I_2(aq) + 2NaCl(aq)$

c. $Ca(s) + H_2O(l) \rightarrow$

Analyze

Step 1. Identify relevant concepts.
In Table 11.2, notice that Ca is more reactive than H and can replace H in water as well as in an acid.

Solve

Step 2. Apply concepts to this situation.
One Ca replaces one H, but notice Ca has a 2+ charge and OH has a 1− charge. Also, hydrogen gas exists as a diatomic molecule. A reaction occurs resulting in the skeleton equation:
$Ca(s) + H_2O(l) \rightarrow H_2(g) + Ca(OH)_2(aq)$

Balancing the equation gives this result.

$Ca(s) + 2H_2O(l) \rightarrow 2H_2(g) + Ca(OH)_2(aq)$

CHAPTER 11, Chemical Reactions *(continued)*

GUIDED PRACTICE PROBLEM 18 (page 335)

18. Write the products of these double-replacement reactions. Balance each
equation.

    a. $NaOH + Fe(NO_3)_3 \rightarrow$ (Iron (III) hydroxide is a precipitate.)

    b. $Ba(NO_3)_2 + H_3PO_4 \rightarrow$ (Barium phosphate is a precipitate.)

a. $NaOH + Fe(NO_3)_3 \rightarrow$

Analyze

Step 1. Identify relevant concepts.
The driving force is the formation of the precipitate iron (III) hydroxide—
$Fe(OH)_3$

Solve

Step 2. Apply concepts to this situation.
Fe and Na replace each other. A reaction occurs resulting in the skeleton equation:

$$NaOH(aq) + Fe(NO_3)_3(aq) \rightarrow Fe(OH)_3(s) + NaNO_3(aq)$$

Balancing this equation gives this result:

$$3NaOH(aq) + Fe(NO_3)_3(aq) \rightarrow Fe(OH)_3(s) + 3NaNO_3(aq)$$

b. $Ba(NO_3)_2 + H_3PO_4 \rightarrow$

Analyze

Step 1. Identify relevant concepts.
The driving force is the formation of the precipitate barium phosphate—
$Ba_3(PO_4)_2$

Solve

Step 2. Apply concepts to this situation.
Ba and H replace each other. A reaction occurs resulting in the skeleton equation:

$$Ba(NO_3)_2(aq) + H_3PO_4(aq) \rightarrow Ba_3(PO_4)_2(s) + HNO_3(aq)$$

Balancing this equation gives the result:

$$3Ba(NO_3)_2(aq) + 2H_3PO_4(aq) \rightarrow Ba_3(PO_4)_2(s) + 6HNO_3(aq)$$

GUIDED PRACTICE PROBLEM 21 (page 337)

21. Write a balanced equation for the complete combustion of glucose ($C_6H_{12}O_6$).

Analyze

Step 1. Identify the relevant concepts.
Oxygen gas is the other reactant in a combustion reaction. The products are CO_2 and H_2O. Write a skeleton equation for this reaction.

$C_6H_{12}O_6 + O_2 \rightarrow CO_2 + H_2O$

Solve

Step 2. Apply concepts to this situation.
Balance the equation.

$C_6H_{12}O_6 + 6O_2 \rightarrow 6CO_2 + 6H_2O$

12 STOICHIOMETRY

SECTION 12.1 THE ARITHMETIC OF EQUATIONS (pages 353–358)

This section explains how to calculate the amount of reactants required or product formed in a nonchemical process. It teaches you how to interpret chemical equations in terms of interacting moles, representative particles, masses, and gas volume at STP.

▶ Using Everyday Equations (pages 353–355)

1. How can you determine the quantities of reactants and products in a chemical reaction?

   You can use the balanced equation.

2. Quantity usually means the _____amount_____ of a substance expressed in grams or moles.

3. A bookcase is to be built from 3 shelves (Sh), 2 side boards (Sb), 1 top (T), 1 base (B), and 4 legs (L). Write a "balanced equation" for the construction of this bookcase.

   $3Sh + 2Sb + T + B + 4L = Sh_3Sb_2TBL_4$

▶ Using Balanced Chemical Equations (page 354)

4. Is the following sentence true or false? Stoichiometry is the calculation of quantities in chemical reactions. _____true_____

5. Calculations using balanced equations are called ___stoichiometric calculations___.

▶ Interpreting Chemical Equations (pages 356–357)

6. From what elements is ammonia produced? How is it used?

   Ammonia molecules are composed of nitrogen and hydrogen; it is used as a fertilizer.

7. Circle the letter of the term that tells what kind of information you CANNOT get from a chemical equation.

   a. moles

   b. mass

   c. size of particles

   d. volume

   e. number of particles

CHAPTER 12, Stoichiometry *(continued)*

8. The coefficients of a balanced chemical equation tell you the relative number of

   moles of _____reactants_____ and _____products_____ in a chemical reaction.

9. Why is the relative number of moles of reactants and products the most important information that a balanced chemical equation provides?

   Knowing the relative number of moles allows you to calculate the amounts of

   reactants and products.

▶ Mass Conservation in Chemical Reactions (pages 357–358)

10. Is the following sentence true or false? A balanced chemical equation must

    obey the law of conservation of mass. _____true_____

11. Use Figure 12.3 on page 357. Complete the table about the reaction of nitrogen and hydrogen.

$N_2(g)$	+	$3H_2(g)$	→	$2NH_3(g)$
2 atoms N	+	6 atoms H	→	2 atoms N and 6 atoms H
1 molecule N_2	+	3 molecules H_2	→	2 molecules NH_3
1 × (6.02×10^{23} molecules N_2)	+	3 × (6.02×10^{23} molecules H_2)	→	2 × (6.02×10^{23} molecules NH_3)
1 mol N_2	+	3 mol H_2	→	2 mol NH_3
28 g N_2	+	3 × 2 g H_2	→	2 × 17 g NH_3
		34 g reactants	→	34 g products
Assume STP 22.4 L N_2	+	67.2 L H_2	→	44.8 L NH_3

12. Circle the letter(s) of the items that are ALWAYS conserved in every chemical reaction.

    a. volume of gases   d. moles

    b. mass   e. molecules

    c. formula units   **f.** atoms

13. What reactant combines with oxygen to form sulfur dioxide? Where can this reactant be found in nature?

    Hydrogen sulfide gas combines with oxygen to form sulfur dioxide. It can be found in

    volcanic areas.

Name _____ Date _____ Class _____

SECTION 12.2 CHEMICAL CALCULATIONS (pages 359–366)

This section shows you how to construct mole ratios from balanced chemical equations. It then teaches you how to calculate stoichiometric quantities from balanced chemical equations using units of moles, mass, representative particles, and volumes of gases at STP.

▶ Writing and Using Mole Ratios (pages 359–362)

1. What is essential for all calculations involving amounts of reactants and products? <u>A balanced chemical equation is essential.</u>

2. Is the following sentence true or false? If you know the number of moles of one substance in a reaction, you need more information than the balanced chemical equation to determine the number of moles of all the other substances in the reaction.

   _____<u>false</u>_____

3. The coefficients from a balanced chemical equation are used to write conversion factors called _____<u>mole ratios</u>_____ .

4. What are mole ratios used for?

   <u>Mole ratios are used to calculate the number of moles of product from a given</u>

   <u>number of moles of reactant or to calculate the number of moles of reactant from</u>

   <u>a given number of moles of product.</u>

   _____

5. The equation for the formation of potassium chloride is given by the equation

   $2K(s) + Cl_2(g) \longrightarrow 2KCl(s)$

   Write the six possible mole ratios for this equation.

   $$\frac{2 \text{ mol K}}{1 \text{ mol Cl}_2} \qquad\qquad \frac{1 \text{ mol Cl}_2}{2 \text{ mol KCl}}$$

   $$\frac{2 \text{ mol K}}{2 \text{ mol KCl}} \qquad\qquad \frac{2 \text{ mol KCl}}{2 \text{ mol K}}$$

   $$\frac{1 \text{ mol Cl}_2}{2 \text{ mol K}} \qquad\qquad \frac{2 \text{ mol KCl}}{1 \text{ mol Cl}_2}$$

6. Is the following sentence true or false? Laboratory balances are used to measure moles of substances directly. _____<u>false</u>_____

7. The amount of a substance is *usually* determined by measuring its mass in _____<u>grams</u>_____ .

CHAPTER 12, Stoichiometry *(continued)*

8. Is the following sentence true or false? If a sample is measured in grams, molar mass can be used to convert the mass to moles. _____true_____

9. Complete the flow chart to show the steps for the mass–mass conversion of any given mass of G to any wanted mass of W. In the chemical equation, a moles of G react with b moles of W.

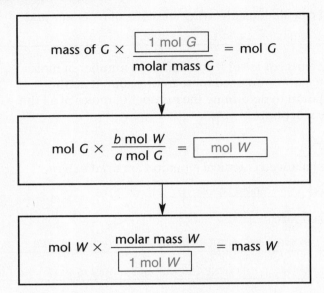

mass of $G \times \dfrac{1 \text{ mol } G}{\text{molar mass } G} = \text{mol } G$

mol $G \times \dfrac{b \text{ mol } W}{a \text{ mol } G} = \boxed{\text{mol } W}$

mol $W \times \dfrac{\text{molar mass } W}{\boxed{1 \text{ mol } W}} = \text{mass } W$

10. Use the diagram below. Describe the steps needed to solve a mass–mass stoichiometry problem.

First convert mass of G to moles of G. Then use the mole ratio to find moles of W.

Finally, convert moles of W to mass of W.

$aG \longrightarrow bW$
(given quantity) **(wanted quantity)**

$\text{mass of } G \times \dfrac{1 \text{ mol } G}{\text{mass } G} \rightarrow \text{mol } G \times \dfrac{b \text{ mol } W}{a \text{ mol } G} \rightarrow \text{mol } W \times \dfrac{\text{mass } W}{1 \text{ mol } W} \rightarrow \text{mass of } W$

▶ Other Stoichiometric Calculations (pages 363–366)

11. Is the following sentence true or false? Stoichiometric calculations can be expanded to include any unit of measurement that is related to the mole.

_____true_____

12. List two or three types of problems that can be solved with stoichiometric calculations.

The problems can include mass–volume, volume–volume, and particle–mass

calculations.

13. In any problem relating to stoichiometric calculations, the given quantity is

first converted to _____ moles _____ .

14. The combustion of methane produces carbon dioxide and water. The chemical equation for this reaction is

$$CH_4(g) + 2O_2(g) \longrightarrow CO_2(g) + 2H_2O(g)$$

Write the three conversion factors you would use to find the volume of carbon dioxide obtained from 1.5 L of oxygen.

$$\frac{1 \text{ mol } O_2}{22.4 \text{ L } O_2} \qquad \frac{1 \text{ mol } CO_2}{2 \text{ mol } O_2} \qquad \frac{22.4 \text{ L } CO_2}{1 \text{ mol } CO_2}$$

Reading Skill Practice

Sometimes information you read is easier to remember if you write it in a different format. For example, the paragraph on page 363 and Figure 12.8 both explain how to solve stoichiometric problems. Use these explanations to make a diagram or flow chart for solving a particle–mass stoichiometry problem. Do your work on a separate sheet of paper.

$$\text{representative particles of } G \times \frac{1 \text{ mol } G}{6.02 \times 10^{23}} \longrightarrow \text{mol } G \times \frac{b \text{ mol } W}{a \text{ mol } G} \longrightarrow \text{mol } W \times \frac{\text{mass } W}{1 \text{ mol } W} = \text{mass of } W$$

SECTION 12.3 LIMITING REAGENT AND PERCENT YIELD (pages 368–375)

This section helps you identify and use the limiting reagent in a reaction to calculate the maximum amount of product(s) produced and the amount of excess reagent. It also explains how to calculate theoretical yield, actual yield, or percent yield, given appropriate information.

▶ Limiting and Excess Reagents (pages 368–371)

1. What is a limiting reagent? A limiting reagent limits or determines the amount of

product that can be formed in a reaction.

2. Is the following sentence true or false? A chemical reaction stops before the

limiting reagent is used up. _____ false _____

3. Circle the letter of the term that correctly completes the sentence. The reactant that is not completely used up in a chemical reaction is called the _____ .

a. spectator reagent   **c.** excess reagent

b. limiting reagent   **d.** catalyst

CHAPTER 12, Stoichiometry *(continued)*

4. If the quantities of reactants are given in units other than moles, what is the first step for determining the amount of product?

   a. Determine the amount of product from the given amount of limiting reagent.

   (b.) Convert each given quantity of reactant to moles.

   c. Identify the limiting reagent.

5. In the diagram below, which reactant is the limiting reagent and why? The chemical equation for the formation of water is $2H_2 + O_2 \longrightarrow 2H_2O$.

   Hydrogen is the limiting reagent, because three hydrogen molecules will combine

   with only three oxygen atoms.

Experimental Conditions		
	Reactants	Products
Before reaction	2 molecules O_2 3 molecules H_2	0 molecules H_2O

▶ Percent Yield (pages 372–375)

6. What is the theoretical yield?

   The theoretical yield is the maximum amount of product that could be formed from

   given amounts of reactants.

7. The amount of product that actually forms when a chemical reaction is carried out in a laboratory is called the _____actual_____ yield.

8. Is the following sentence true or false? The actual yield is usually greater than the theoretical yield. _____false_____

9. Complete the equation for the percent yield of a chemical reaction.

$$\text{Percent yield} = \frac{\boxed{\text{actual}} \text{ yield}}{\boxed{\text{theoretical}} \text{ yield}} \times 100\%$$

10. Describe four factors that may cause percent yields to be less than 100%.

    impure reactants, competing side reactions, loss of product during filtration or in

    transferring between containers, carelessly measuring reactants or products

GUIDED PRACTICE PROBLEMS

GUIDED PRACTICE PROBLEM 11 (page 360)

11. This equation shows the formation of aluminum oxide.

$$4Al(s) + 3O_2(g) \longrightarrow 2Al_2O_3(s)$$

a. How many moles of oxygen are required to react completely with 14.8 moles of aluminum?

Analyze

1. What is the given information? _____14.8 mol Al_____

2. What is the unknown? _____moles of O_2_____

3. What conversion factor will you need to use? _____$\dfrac{3 \text{ mol } O_2}{4 \text{ mol Al}}$_____

Calculate

4. Complete the solution. 14.8 _____mol Al_____ $\times$ $\dfrac{3 \text{ mol } O_2}{\boxed{4 \text{ mol Al}}}$ = _____11.1_____ mol O_2

Evaluate

5. Why does the answer have three significant figures?

Because the moles of aluminum is given to three significant figures, and because

defined numbers such as mole ratios have an infinite number of significant figures.

_____

b. How many moles of aluminum oxide are formed when 0.78 moles of oxygen react with an excess of aluminum?

Analyze

6. What information is given? _____0.78 mol O_2_____

7. What information is unknown? _____moles of Al_2O_3_____

Calculate

8. Complete the solution. _____0.78_____ mol O_2 $\times$ $\dfrac{\boxed{2} \text{ mol } Al_2O_3}{\boxed{3 \text{ mol } O_2}}$

= _____0.52_____ mol Al_2O_3

Evaluate

9. Why does the answer have two significant figures?

The answer has two significant figures because the number of moles of oxygen has

two significant figures.

CHAPTER 12, Stoichiometry *(continued)*

EXTRA PRACTICE (similar to Practice Problem 15, page 364)

15. How many molecules of oxygen are produced by the decomposition of 1225 grams of potassium chlorate ($KClO_3$)?

$$2KClO_3(s) \longrightarrow 2KCl(s) + 3O_2(g)$$

$$1225 \text{ g } KClO_3 \times \frac{1 \text{ mol } KClO_3}{122.5 \text{ g } KClO_3} \times \frac{3 \text{ mol } O_2}{2 \text{ mol } KClO_3} \times \frac{6.02 \times 10^{23} \text{ molecules } O_2}{1 \text{ mol } O_2}$$

$$= 15 \times 6.02 \times 10^{23} \text{ molecules } O_2 = 9.03 \times 10^{24} \text{ molecules } O_2$$

EXTRA PRACTICE (similar to Practice Problem 17, page 365)

17. The equation for the combustion of carbon monoxide is

$$2CO(g) + O_2(g) \longrightarrow 2CO_2(g)$$

How many liters of oxygen are needed to burn 10 liters of carbon monoxide?

$$10 \text{ L } CO \times \frac{1 \text{ mol } CO}{22.4 \text{ L } CO} \times \frac{1 \text{ mol } O_2}{2 \text{ mol } CO} \times \frac{22.4 \text{ L } O_2}{1 \text{ mol } O_2} = 5 \text{ L } O_2$$

GUIDED PRACTICE PROBLEM 25 (page 370)

25. The equation for the complete combustion of ethene (C_2H_4) is

$$C_2H_4(g) + 3O_2(g) \longrightarrow 2CO_2(g) + 2H_2O(g)$$

a. If 2.70 moles of ethene reacted with 6.30 moles of oxygen, identify the limiting reagent.

Step 1. Calculate the number of moles of oxygen needed to react with 2.70 moles of ethane. Multiply by the mole ratio.

$$2.70 \underline{\quad \text{mol } C_2H_4 \quad} \times \frac{\boxed{3} \text{ mol } O_2}{1 \text{ mol } C_2H_4}$$

$$= \underline{\quad 8.10 \quad} \text{ mol } O_2$$

Step 2. Compare the number of moles of oxygen needed to the number given.

$\underline{\quad 6.30 \text{ mol} \quad}$ O_2 given is less than

$\underline{\quad 8.10 \quad}$ mol O_2 needed

Step 3. Identify the limiting reagent.

Because $\underline{\quad 8.10 \quad}$ mol O_2 are needed

to react with the 2.70 mol C_2H_4 and

only $\underline{\quad 6.30 \quad}$ mol O_2 are available,

$\underline{\quad \text{oxygen} \quad}$ is the limiting reagent.

---

b. Calculate the number of moles of water produced.

| **Step 1.** Identify the mole ratio needed. | $\dfrac{\boxed{2}\ \text{mol H}_2\text{O}}{3\ \text{mol O}_2}$ |

Step 2. Calculate the given number of moles of oxygen.

$$6.30\ \underline{\text{mol O}_2} \times \dfrac{\boxed{2}\ \text{mol H}_2\text{O}}{3\ \text{mol O}_2}$$

$$=\underline{4.20}\ \text{mol H}_2\text{O}$$

GUIDED PRACTICE PROBLEM 29 (page 374)

29. When 84.8 grams of iron(III) oxide reacts with an excess of carbon monoxide, 54.3 grams of iron are produced.

$$\text{Fe}_2\text{O}_3(s) + 3\text{CO}(g) \longrightarrow 2\text{Fe}(s) + 3\text{CO}_2(g)$$

What is the percent yield of this reaction?

Step 1. First calculate the theoretical yield. Begin by finding the molar mass of Fe_2O_3.

2 mol Fe × (_55.8_ g Fe/mol Fe) +

3 mol O$_3$ × (_16.0_ g O$_3$/mol O$_3$)

= _111.6_ g + 48.0 g

= _159.6_ g

Step 2. Calculate the number of moles of iron(III) oxide. Multiply by the mole/mass conversion factor.

_84.8_ g Fe$_2$O$_3$ × $\dfrac{1\ \text{mol Fe}_2\text{O}_3}{159.6\ \text{g Fe}_2\text{O}_3}$

= _0.531_ mol

Step 3. Find the number of moles of Fe expected. Multiply by the mole ratio.

0.531 _mol Fe$_2$O$_3$_ × $\dfrac{\boxed{2}\ \text{mol Fe}}{1\ \text{mol Fe}_2\text{O}_3}$

= _1.062_ mol Fe

Step 4. Find the mass of iron that should be produced. Multiply by the mole/mass conversion factor.

1.062 _mol Fe_ × $\dfrac{\boxed{55.8}\ \text{g Fe}}{1\ \text{mol Fe}}$ = 59.3 g Fe

Step 5. Compare the actual yield to the theoretical yield by dividing.

$\dfrac{\text{actual yield}}{\text{theoretical yield}} = \dfrac{\boxed{54.3}\ \text{g Fe}}{\boxed{59.3}\ \text{g Fe}}$ = 0.916

Step 6. Write the answer as a percent, with the correct number of significant figures.

0.916 = _91.6%_

STATES OF MATTER

13

SECTION 13.1 THE NATURE OF GASES (pages 385–389)

This section introduces the kinetic theory and describes how it applies to gases. It defines gas pressure and explains how temperature is related to the kinetic energy of the particles of a substance.

▶ **Kinetic Theory and a Model for Gases** (pages 385–386)

1. The energy an object has because of its motion is called
   _____ kinetic energy _____ .

2. Circle the letter of each sentence that is true about the assumptions of the kinetic theory concerning gases.

   a. A gas is composed of particles with insignificant volume that are relatively far apart from each other.

   b. Strong attractive forces exist between particles of a gas.

   c. Gases tend to collect near the bottom of a container.

   d. The paths of uninterrupted travel of particles in a gas are relatively short because the particles are constantly colliding with each other or with other objects.

3. Is the following statement true or false? According to the kinetic theory, collisions between particles in a gas are perfectly elastic because kinetic energy is transferred without loss from one particle to another, and the total kinetic energy remains constant. _____ true _____

▶ **Gas Pressure** (pages 386–387)

4. Gas pressure results from the force exerted by a gas per _____ unit surface _____
   area of an object _____ .

5. Simultaneous collisions of billions of particles in a gas with an object result in _____ gas pressure _____ .

6. What force holds the particles of air in Earth's atmosphere? _____ gravity _____

7. What kind of pressure is measured with a barometer?
   atmospheric pressure _____

CHAPTER 13, States of Matter *(continued)*

8. Look at Figure 13.2 on page 386. What accounts for the difference in height of the two mercury columns shown in the figure?

The mercury column on the left is shown at sea level; the one on the right is shown

at an altitude of 9000 m. Because atmospheric pressure decreases as altitude

increases, the column on the right is lower than the one on the left.

_____

9. Circle the letter next to every name of a unit of pressure.

(a.) mm Hg   **(d.)** kPa

b. standard   **(e.)** atm

(c.) pascal   **f.** degree

10. Standard temperature and pressure (STP) are defined as _____ a temperature _____

of 0°C and a pressure of 101.3 kPa or 1 atm

▶ Kinetic Energy and Temperature (pages 388–389)

11. What happens to the temperature of a substance when the average kinetic energy of its particles increases?

The temperature of the substance increases.

12. Is the following statement true or false. All the particles in a substance at a

given temperature have the same kinetic energy. _____ false _____

13. The temperature 0K, or −273.15°C, is called _____ kinetic energy _____ zero.

Theoretically, particles of matter at this temperature would have no _____ kinetic energy/motion _____.

14. On the graph below, write the labels *lower temperature* and *higher temperature* to identify the curve that depicts the kinetic energy distribution of particles in a liquid at a lower temperature and at a higher temperature.

15. Circle the letter of the temperature scale that correctly completes this sentence. Temperature on the _____ scale is directly proportional to the average kinetic energy of the particles of a substance.

 a. Celsius

 (b.) Kelvin

 c. Fahrenheit

 d. Centigrade

SECTION 13.2 THE NATURE OF LIQUIDS (pages 390–395)

This section describes a model for liquids in terms of kinetic energy and the attractive forces between the particles in a liquid. It also uses kinetic theory to distinguish evaporation from boiling.

▶ A Model for Liquids (page 390)

1. Is the following sentence true or false? The kinetic theory states that there are no attractions between the particles of a liquid.

 _____ false _____

2. Circle the letter next to each sentence that is true about the particles of a liquid.

 a. Most of the particles in a liquid have enough kinetic energy to escape into a gaseous state.

 (b.) Liquids are much denser than gases because intermolecular forces reduce the amount of space between the particles in a liquid.

 (c.) Increasing pressure on a liquid has hardly any effect on its volume.

 (d.) Liquid particles are free to slide past one another.

▶ Evaporation (page 391)

3. The conversion of a liquid to a gas or vapor is called _____ vaporization _____ .

4. When vaporization occurs at the surface of a liquid that is not boiling, the process is called _____ evaporation _____ .

5. As a liquid evaporates, why do only some of the particles break away from the surface of the liquid? Why does the liquid evaporate faster if the temperature is increased?

 Most of the molecules do not have enough kinetic energy to overcome the attractive

 forces. As the temperature is increased, the average kinetic energy increases and

 more particles have enough kinetic energy to overcome the forces keeping them in

 the liquid state.

 _____

CHAPTER 13, States of Matter *(continued)*

6. Is the following sentence true or false? Evaporation is a cooling process because the particles in a liquid with the highest kinetic energy tend to escape first, leaving the remaining particles with a lower average kinetic energy and, thus, a lower temperature. _____true_____

Questions 7, 8, 9, and 10 refer to either container A or container B below. Think of each container as a system involving both liquid water and water vapor.

(a)

(b)

7. From which of the containers are water molecules able to escape? _b_

8. In which container can a dynamic equilibrium between water molecules in the liquid state and water molecules in the vapor state be established? _a_

9. In which container will the water level remain constant? _a_

10. From which container is it possible for all of the liquid water to disappear through evaporation? _b_

11. What causes the chill you may feel after stepping out of a swimming pool on a warm, windy day?

Wind causes water on the skin to evaporate, which is a cooling process.

_____

_____

▶ **Vapor Pressure** (pages 392–393)

12. Circle the letter next to each sentence that is true about vapor pressure.

(**a.**) Vapor pressure arises when particles of a liquid in a closed, partly filled container vaporize and collide with the walls of the container.

(**b.**) After a time in a closed, partly filled container, a liquid will evaporate and its vapor will condense at equal rates.

c. Look at Figure 13.6b on page 391. Condensation on the inside of the terrarium indicates that there is not a liquid-vapor equilibrium in the sealed terrarium.

(**d.**) When the temperature of a contained liquid increases, its vapor pressure increases.

13. Look at Figure 13.7 on page 393. How does the vapor pressure of the ethanol in the manometer change when the temperature is increased from 0°C to 20°C? Circle the letter of the correct answer.

a. The vapor pressure decreases by more than 4 kPa.

b. The vapor pressure remains constant.

(**c.**) The vapor pressure increases by more than 4 kPa.

d. There is no way to detect a change in vapor pressure with a manometer.

▶ **Boiling Point** (pages 393–395)

14. The boiling point of a liquid is the temperature at which the vapor pressure of the liquid is just equal to the _____ external pressure _____.

15. Look at Figure 13.8 on page 394. Why does the boiling point decrease as altitude increases?

At higher altitudes, atmospheric pressure is lower than it is at sea level. Because

boiling occurs when vapor pressure is equal to atmospheric pressure, a liquid boils

at a lower temperature.

16. Use Figure 13.9 on page 394. At approximately what temperature would ethanol boil atop Mount Everest, where the atmospheric pressure is 34 kPa? Circle the letter next to the best estimate.

(**a.**) 50°C   **b.** 100°C   **c.** 0°C   **d.** 85°C

17. Is the following sentence true or false? After a liquid reaches its boiling point, its temperature continues to rise until all the liquid vaporizes. _____ false _____

CHAPTER 13, States of Matter *(continued)*

Reading Skill Practice

Writing a summary can help you remember what you have read. When you write a summary, include only the most important points. Write a summary of the discussion of boiling point on pages 393–395. Do your work on a separate sheet of paper.

Students' summaries should include a definition of boiling point and normal boiling point. They should also include the effects of pressure on the temperature of a boiling liquid.

SECTION 13.3 THE NATURE OF SOLIDS (pages 396–399)

This section describes the highly organized structures of solids, distinguishes between a crystal lattice and a unit cell, and explains how allotropes of an element differ.

▶ A Model for Solids (page 396)

1. Is the following sentence true or false? Although particles in solids have kinetic energy, the motion of particles in solids is restricted to vibrations about fixed points. _____true_____

2. A solid melts when _____the organization of its particles breaks down_____.

3. Is the following sentence true or false? The temperature at which the liquid and solid states of a substance are in equilibrium is the same as the melting point *and* the freezing point of the substance. _____true_____

▶ Crystal Structure and Unit Cells (pages 396–399)

4. How are particles arranged in a crystal?

   They are arranged in an orderly, repeating, three-dimensional pattern.

5. What type of solid has a relatively low melting point?

   A molecular solid has a relatively low melting point.

6. Do all solids melt when heated? Explain.

   No; some solids, such as wood, decompose.

7. Circle the letter next to each sentence that is true about solids.

   a. Most solid substances are not crystalline.

   (b.) All crystals have sides, or faces, that intersect at angles that are characteristic for a given substance.

   (c.) There are seven groups, or crystal systems, into which all crystals may be classified.

   (d.) The orderly array of sodium ions and chloride ions gives crystals of table salt their regular shape.

Identify the unit cell in each figure below as simple cubic, body-centered cubic, or face-centered cubic.

8. __face-centered cubic__   9. __body-centered cubic__   10. __simple cubic__

11. Is the following sentence true or false? Some solid substances can exist in more than one form. Give an example to support your answer.

   True. The element carbon has at least three solid forms: graphite, diamond, and

   buckminsterfullerene.

12. Two or more different molecular forms of the same element in the same

   physical state are called _____allotropes_____ .

13. What is an amorphous solid?

   An amorphous solid lacks an ordered internal structure.

14. Circle the letter next to each solid that is an amorphous solid.

   a. table salt   **c.** plastic

   b. rubber   **d.** glass

15. How are glasses different from crystalline solids?

   The internal structures of glasses are intermediate between free-flowing liquids

   and crystalline solids. Glasses do not have a definite melting point, but soften

   when heated. Glass breaks into irregular, jagged pieces when shattered.

SECTION 13.4 CHANGES OF STATE (pages 401–404)

This section describes the process of sublimation. It also explains phase changes between solid, liquid, and vapor states and how to interpret a phase diagram.

▶ Sublimation (page 401)

1. The process by which wet laundry dries on an outdoor clothesline in winter

   is called _____sublimation_____ .

2. Is the following sentence true or false? Solids have vapor pressure because

   some particles near the surface of a solid substance have enough kinetic

   energy to escape directly into the vapor phase. _____true_____

CHAPTER 13, States of Matter *(continued)*

▶ Phase Diagrams (pages 402–403)

3. What does a phase diagram show?

A phase diagram shows the temperature and pressure conditions at which a

substance exists in the solid, liquid, and vapor phases.

4. What is the triple point of a substance?

The triple point represents the only conditions of temperature and pressure at

which three phases of a substance can exist in equilibrium.

5. In the phase diagram for water shown below, label the melting point and boiling point at normal atmospheric pressure, and the triple point.

6. Use the phase diagram above to answer the following question. Why is a laboratory required to produce the conditions necessary for observing water at the triple point?

From the diagram, the triple point of water is at a pressure of 0.61 kPa, far below

atmospheric pressure. Laboratory equipment is necessary to achieve pressures this low.

GUIDED PRACTICE PROBLEM

GUIDED PRACTICE PROBLEM 2 (page 387)

2. The pressure at the top of Mount Everest is 33.7 kPa. Is that pressure greater than or less than 0.25 atm?

Analyze

Step 1. To convert kPa to atm, what conversion factor do you need to use?

$$\frac{1 \text{ atm}}{101.3 \text{ kPa}}$$

Step 2. Why can you use an estimate to solve this problem?

Because "greater than or less than" questions don't require an exact answer. An

estimate will probably be sufficient to produce the correct answer.

Calculate

Step 3. Write the expression needed to find the answer.

$$33.7 \text{ kPa} \times \frac{1 \text{ atm}}{101.3 \text{ kPa}} = \frac{33.7}{101.3} \text{ atm}$$

Step 4. Which common fraction is this number close to?

$\frac{33.7}{101.3}$ atm is close to $\frac{33}{99}$ atm or $\frac{1}{3}$ atm.

Step 5. What is this fraction written as a decimal? Is this number greater than or less than 0.25?

0.333 is greater than 0.25.

Evaluate

Step 6. Are you confident your estimate gave a correct answer to this problem?

Because the estimate is more than 30% greater than 0.25, you can be confident

that the difference isn't due to rounding.

EXTRA PRACTICE (similar to Practice Problem 1, page 387)

1. What pressure, in atmospheres, does a gas exert at 152 mm Hg?

$$152 \text{ mm Hg} \times \frac{1 \text{ atm}}{760 \text{ mm Hg}} = 0.200 \text{ atm}$$

What is this pressure in kilopascals?

$$0.200 \text{ atm} \times \frac{101.3 \text{ kPa}}{1 \text{ atm}} = 20.3 \text{ kPa}$$

14 THE BEHAVIOR OF GASES

SECTION 14.1 PROPERTIES OF GASES (pages 413–417)

This section uses kinetic theory to explain the properties of gases. This section also explains how gas pressure is affected by the amount of gas, its volume, and its temperature.

▶ Compressibility (pages 413–414)

1. Look at Figure 14.1 on page 413. How does an automobile air bag protect the crash dummy from being broken as a result of impact?

   The gases used to inflate the airbag are able to absorb a considerable amount

   of energy when they are compressed.

   _____

2. What theory explains the behavior of gases? _____ kinetic theory _____

3. Circle the letter next to each sentence that is true concerning the compressibility of gases.

   (a.) The large relative distances between particles in a gas means that there is considerable empty space between the particles.

   (b.) The assumption that particles in a gas are relatively far apart explains gas compressibility.

   (c.) Compressibility is a measure of how much the volume of matter decreases under pressure.

   d. Energy is released by a gas when it is compressed.

▶ Factors Affecting Gas Pressure (pages 414–417)

4. List the name, the symbol, and a common unit for the four variables that are generally used to describe the characteristics of a gas.

   a. _____ pressure, *P*, kilopascals _____

   b. _____ volume, *V*, liters _____

   c. _____ temperature, *T*, kelvins _____

   d. _____ amount of gas, *n*, moles _____

5. What keeps the raft in Figure 14.3 inflated?

   The air pressure exerted by the enclosed gas keeps the raft inflated.

   _____

CHAPTER 14, The Behavior of Gases *(continued)*

6. How do conditions change inside a rigid container when you use a pump to add gas to the container?

Because particles are added to the container, the pressure increases inside the

container.

7. The diagrams below show a sealed container at three pressures. Complete the labels showing the gas pressure in each container.

100 kPa

150 kPa

200 kPa

N particles   1.5*N* particles   2*N* particles

8. What can happen if too much gas is pumped into a sealed, rigid container?

The pressure inside the container can increase beyond the strength of its walls,

causing the container to rupture or burst.

9. Is the following sentence true or false? When a sealed container of gas is opened, gas will flow from the region of lower pressure to the region of higher pressure. _____false_____

10. Look at Figure 14.5 on page 416. What happens when the push button on an aerosol spray can is pressed?

Pushing the button creates an opening between the atmosphere and the gas inside

the can, which is at a higher pressure. Gas from inside the can rushes out of the

opening, forcing the product in the can out with it.

11. In the diagram, complete the labels showing the pressure on the piston and the gas pressure inside the container.

100 kPa

100 kPa

200 kPa

200 kPa

Volume = 2.0 L

Volume = 1.0 L

12. When the volume is reduced by one half, what happens to the pressure?

The pressure will double.

13. Is the following sentence true or false? Raising the temperature of a

contained gas causes its pressure to decrease. _____false_____

14. Circle the letter next to each sentence that correctly describes how gases behave when the temperature increases.

(a.) The average kinetic energy of the particles in the gas increases as the particles absorb energy.

(b.) Faster-moving particles impact the walls of their container with more force, exerting greater pressure.

c. When the average kinetic energy of the enclosed particles doubles, temperature doubles and the pressure is cut in half.

15. Explain why it is dangerous to throw aerosol cans into a fire.

Throwing an aerosol can into a fire causes the gas pressure inside the can to

increase greatly, with the likelihood that the can will burst.

16. Decide whether the following sentence is true or false, and explain your reasoning. When the temperature of a sample of steam increases from 100°C to 200°C, the average kinetic energy of its particles doubles.

False. For average kinetic energy to double, the temperature must increase from

100°C (373 K) to 473°C (746 K).

SECTION 14.2 THE GAS LAWS (pages 418–425)

This section explains the relationships among the volume, pressure, and temperature of gases as described by Boyle's law, Charles's law, Gay-Lussac's law, and the combined gas law.

▶ Boyle's Law: Pressure and Volume (pages 418–419)

1. Circle the letter of each sentence that is true about the relationship between the volume and the pressure of a contained gas at constant temperature.

(a.) When the pressure increases, the volume decreases.

(b.) When the pressure decreases, the volume increases.

c. When the pressure increases, the volume increases.

d. When the pressure decreases, the volume decreases.

2. _____Boyle's_____ law states that for a given mass of gas at constant temperature, the volume of the gas varies inversely with pressure.

CHAPTER 14, The Behavior of Gases *(continued)*

Questions 3, 4, 5, and 6 refer to the graph. This graph represents the relationship between pressure and volume for a sample of gas in a container at a constant temperature.

3. $P_1 \times V_1 = $ _____160 kPa $\times$ 2.0 L_____

4. $P_2 \times V_2 = $ _____50 kPa $\times$ 4.0 L_____

5. $P_3 \times V_3 = $ _____200 kPa $\times$ 1.0 L_____

6. What do you notice about the product of pressure times volume at constant temperature?

   Pressure times volume is constant.

▶ Charles's Law: Temperature and Volume (pages 420–421)

7. Look at the graph in Figure 14.10 on page 420. What two observations did Jacques Charles make about the behavior of gases from similar data?

   The graphs for volume versus temperature of any gas is a straight line, and all the

   lines intersect the temperature axis at the same point, –273.15°C.

8. What does it mean to say that two variables are directly proportional?

   When one variable increases, the other increases so that the ratio of the two

   variables remains constant.

9. Is the following sentence true or false? Charles's law states that when the pressure of a fixed mass of gas is held constant, the volume of the gas is directly proportional to its Kelvin temperature. _____true_____

10. Charles's law may be written $\dfrac{V_1}{T_1} = \dfrac{V_2}{T_2}$ at constant pressure if the temperatures are measured on what scale? _____Kelvin_____

▶ Gay-Lussac's Law: Pressure and Temperature (pages 422–423)

11. Complete the following sentence. Gay-Lussac's law states that the pressure of a gas is _directly proportional to the Kelvin temperature if the volume is constant_ .

12. Gay-Lussac's law may be written $\dfrac{P_1}{T_1} = \dfrac{P_2}{T_2}$ if the volume is constant and if the temperatures are measured on what scale? _____the Kelvin scale_____

Name _____ Date _____ Class _____

13. Complete the missing labels in the diagram below showing the pressure change when a gas is heated at constant volume.

100 kPa

300 K

1 L

200 kPa

600 K

1 L

▶ The Combined Gas Law (pages 424–425)

14. Is the following sentence true or false? The gas laws of Boyle, Charles, and Gay-Lussac can be combined into a single mathematical expression.

_____ true _____

Questions 15, 16, 17, and 18 refer to the following equation

$$\frac{P_1 \times V_1}{T_1} = \frac{P_2 \times V_2}{T_2}$$

15. What law does this mathematical equation represent?

the combined gas law

16. Which gas law does this equation represent if temperature is held constant so that $T_1 = T_2$? _____ Boyle's law _____

17. Which gas law does this equation represent if pressure is held constant so that $P_1 = P_2$? _____ Charles's law _____

18. Which gas law does this equation represent if volume is held constant so that $V_1 = V_2$? _____ Gay-Lussac's law _____

19. In which situations does the combined gas law enable you to do calculations when the other gas laws do not apply?

The combined gas law allows calculations for situations where none of the

variables—pressure, temperature, or volume—are constant.

CHAPTER 14, The Behavior of Gases *(continued)*

SECTION 14.3 IDEAL GASES (pages 426–429)

This section explains how to use the ideal gas law to calculate the amount of gas at specified conditions of temperature, pressure and volume. This section also distinguishes real gases from ideal gases.

▶ **Ideal Gas Law** (pages 426–427)

1. In addition to pressure, temperature, and volume, what fourth variable must be considered when analyzing the behavior of a gas?

   The fourth variable is the amount of gas.

2. Is the number of moles in a sample of gas directly proportional or inversely proportional to the number of particles of gas in the sample?

   directly proportional

3. At a specified temperature and pressure, is the number of moles of gas in a sample directly proportional or inversely proportional to the volume of

   the sample? ___directly proportional___

4. Circle the letter next to the correct description of how the combined gas law must be modified to introduce the number of moles.

   a. Multiply each side of the equation by the number of moles.

   b. Add the number of moles to each side of the equation.

   c. Divide each side of the equation by the number of moles.

5. For what kind of gas is $(P \times V)/(T \times n)$ a constant for all values of pressure,

   temperature, and volume under which the gas can exist? ___an ideal gas___

6. What constant can you calculate when you know the volume occupied by one mole of gas at standard temperature and pressure?

   ___*R*, the gas constant___

7. Complete the table about the ideal gas law. Write what each symbol in the ideal gas law represents, the unit in which it is measured and the abbreviation of the unit.

Symbol	Quantity	Unit	Abbreviation for Unit
P	pressure	kilopascals	kPa
V	volume	liters	L
n	amount of gas	moles	mol
R	gas constant	$\dfrac{\text{liters} \times \text{kilopascals}}{\text{kelvins} \times \text{moles}}$	$\dfrac{\text{L} \bullet \text{kPa}}{\text{K} \bullet \text{mol}}$
T	temperature	kelvins	K

8. When would you use the ideal gas law instead of the combined gas law?

The ideal gas law lets you calculate the number of moles of gas at any specified

values of *P*, *V*, and *T*.

▶ Ideal Gases and Real Gases (pages 428–429)

9. Circle the letter of each sentence that is true about ideal gases and real gases.

   a. An ideal gas does not follow the gas laws at all temperatures and pressures.

   b. An ideal gas does not conform to the assumptions of the kinetic theory.

   c. There is no real gas that conforms to the kinetic theory under all conditions of temperature and pressure.

   d. At many conditions of temperature and pressure, real gases behave very much like ideal gases.

10. Is the following sentence true or false? If a gas were truly an ideal gas, it would be impossible to liquefy or solidify it by cooling or by applying pressure.

   _____ true _____

11. Red gases differ most from an ideal gas at _____ low _____ temperatures and

   _____ high _____ pressures.

12. Look at Figure 14.14 on page 428. What substance is shown? What change of state is occurring? How do you know this substance is not an ideal gas?

   The material is liquid nitrogen. It is changing from a liquid to a gas. An ideal gas

   could not be changed from a gas to a liquid.

CHAPTER 14, The Behavior of Gases *(continued)*

SECTION 14.4 GASES: MIXTURES AND MOVEMENTS
(pages 432–436)

This section explains Dalton's law of partial pressures, and Graham's law of effusion.

▶ **Dalton's Law** (pages 432–434)

1. Is the following statement true or false? Gas pressure depends only on the number of particles in a given volume and on their average kinetic energy. The type of particle does not matter. _____true_____

2. The contribution of the pressure of each gas in a mixture to the total pressure is called the _____partial pressure_____ exerted by that gas.

3. What is Dalton's law of partial pressures?

   At constant volume and temperature, the total pressure exerted by a mixture of gases

   is equal to the sum of the partial pressures of the component gases.

4. Container (T) in the figure below contains a mixture of the three different gases in (a), (b), and (c) at the pressures shown. Write in the pressure in container (T).

300 kPa   750 kPa   600 kPa   1650 kPa

(a)   (b)   (c)   (T)

▶ Graham's Law (pages 435–436)

5. The tendency of molecules in a gas to move from areas of higher concentration to areas of lower concentration is called _____ diffusion _____ .

6. What is Graham's law of effusion?

   Graham's law of effusion states that the rate of effusion of a gas is

   inversely proportional to the square root of the gas's molar mass.

7. Is the following sentence true or false? If two objects with different masses have the same kinetic energy, the one with the greater mass must move faster.

   _____ false _____

 # Reading Skill Practice

You may sometimes forget the meaning of a vocabulary term that was introduced earlier in the textbook. When this happens, you can check its meaning in the Glossary on pages R108–R118 of the Reference Section. The Glossary lists all vocabulary terms in the textbook and their meanings. You'll find the terms listed in alphabetical order. Use the Glossary to review the meanings of all vocabulary terms introduced in Section 14.4. Write each term and its definition on a separate sheet of paper.

The wording of the definitions in the Glossary are often slightly different than how the terms are defined in the flow of the text. Students should write the Glossary definition of each term.

CHAPTER 14, The Behavior of Gases *(continued)*

GUIDED PRACTICE PROBLEMS

GUIDED PRACTICE PROBLEM 13 (page 424)

13. A gas at 155 kPa and 25°C has an initial volume of 1.00 L. The pressure of the gas increases to 605 kPa as the temperature is raised to 125°C. What is the new volume?

Analyze

a. Temperature can be converted from Celsius to Kelvin by adding __273__ .

b. What is the expression for the combined gas law?

$$\frac{P_1 \times V_1}{T_1} = \frac{P_2 \times V_2}{T_2}$$

c. What is the unknown in this problem? __V_2__

Calculate

d. Convert degrees Celsius to kelvins.

$T_1 = 25°C + \boxed{273} = \boxed{298}$ K

$T_2 = 125°C + \boxed{273} = \boxed{398}$ K

e. Rearrange the combined gas law to isolate V_2.

$$V_2 = \frac{V_1 \times P_1 \times T_2}{P_2 \times T_1}$$

f. Substitute the known quantities into the equation and solve.

$$V_2 = \frac{1.00 \text{ L} \times \boxed{155} \text{ kPa} \times 398 \text{ K}}{605 \text{ kPa} \times \boxed{298} \text{ K}} = \boxed{0.342 \text{ L}}$$

Evaluate

g. Explain why you think your answer is reasonable.

The new volume is directly proportional to the change in temperature but inversely proportional to the change in pressure. The temperature increased by a multiple of about $\frac{4}{3}$, but the inverse of the pressure change is $\frac{1}{4}$, giving a product of $\frac{1}{3}$. Therefore, the new volume should be about $\frac{1}{3}$ the original volume.

h. Are the units in your answer correct? How do you know?

Yes, because volume is measured in liters.

EXTRA PRACTICE (similar to Practice Problem 11, page 423)

11. A gas has a pressure of 7.50 kPa at 420 K. What will the pressure be at 210 K if the volume does not change?

$$P_2 = \frac{7.50 \text{ kPa} \times 210 \text{ K}}{420 \text{ K}} = 3.8 \text{ kPa}$$

GUIDED PRACTICE PROBLEM 31 (page 434)

31. Determine the total pressure of a gas mixture that contains oxygen, nitrogen, and helium if the partial pressures of the gases are as follows:

$P_{O_2} = 20.0$ kPa, $P_{N_2} = 46.7$ kPa, and $P_{He} = 26.7$ kPa.

Analyze

a. What is the expression for Dalton's law of partial pressure?

$$P_{total} = P_1 + P_2 + P_3$$

b. What is the unknown in this problem? _____ P_{total} _____

Calculate

c. Substitute the known quantities into the equation and solve.

$$P_{total} = 20.0 \text{ kPa} + 46.7 \text{ kPa} + 26.7 \text{ kPa} = 93.4 \text{ kPa}$$

Evaluate

d. Why is your answer reasonable?

The total pressure can be estimated to be 20 + 50 + 25 = 95. The answer 93.4

is close to the estimate of 95.

15 WATER AND AQUEOUS SYSTEMS

SECTION 15.1 WATER AND ITS PROPERTIES (pages 445–449)

This section describes the properties of water in the liquid and solid states and explains how hydrogen bonding affects the surface tension and vapor pressure of water.

▶ Water in the Liquid State (pages 445–447)

1. What unique substance is essential to all life on Earth?

   _____ water _____

2. Approximately what fraction of Earth's surface is covered in water? ____ 3/4 ____

3. Circle the letter next to each sentence that is true concerning water molecules.

   a. Each O — H covalent bond in a water molecule is nonpolar.

   (b.) In a water molecule, the less electronegative hydrogen atoms acquire a partial positive charge and the oxygen atom acquires a partial negative charge.

   (c.) Because the water molecule has an H — O — H bond angle of 105°, the molecule as a whole is polar.

4. The diagram below depicts a water molecule. Complete the labels showing the locations of the hydrogen atoms, the oxygen atom, and the regions of positive and negative charge.

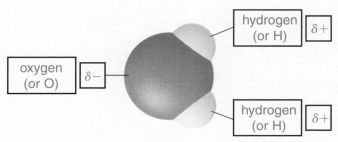

5. The diagram below depicts a collection of water molecules. Draw dotted lines showing where hydrogen bonding occurs.

CHAPTER 15, Water and Aqueous Systems *(continued)*

6. Circle the letter next to each sentence that describes a result of the surface tension of water.

   (a.) In a full glass of water, the water surface seems to bulge over the rim of the glass.

   b. Water beads up into small, nearly spherical drops on a paper towel.

   (c.) Water forms nearly spherical drops at the end of an eyedropper.

   (d.) An insect called a water strider is able to "walk" on water.

7. Using Figure 15.4 on page 447, explain why a water drop has surface tension.

   <u>Because water molecules at the surface cannot form hydrogen bonds with air</u>

   <u>molecules, molecules on the surface are drawn into the body of liquid. The inward pull</u>

   <u>on the molecules is surface tension.</u>

8. Do liquids that have higher surface tension produce drops that are flatter or more nearly spherical than liquids with lower surface tension?

   <u>Liquids with higher surface tension produce drops that are more nearly spherical.</u>

   _____

9. What is the name for an agent, such as a detergent, that has the ability to reduce surface tension? _____ surfactant _____

▶ Water in the Solid State (pages 448–449)

10. What happens to the density of most substances as they cool and solidify?

    <u>Density usually increases as a substance cools.</u>

    _____

11. The diagrams below show hydrogen bonding between water molecules.

Hydrogen bonds

(i)   (ii)

a. Which diagram depicts ice? _____(i)_____

b. Which diagram depicts liquid water? _____(ii)_____

c. Why is ice less dense than liquid water? Refer to the diagrams to help you

explain. _Ice molecules are arranged in an open rigid framework as shown in_

diagram (i). When ice melts, the framework collapses, as shown in diagram (ii),

and the molecules pack closer together.

12. Look at Table 15.1 on page 448. To four significant figures, list the density of

a. liquid water at 4°C _____1.000 g/cm³_____

b. liquid water at 0°C _____0.9998 g/cm³_____

c. ice at 0°C _____0.9168 g/cm³_____

13. What is unusual about the data in Question 12? Will ice float on liquid water?

The density of liquid water decreases from 4°C to 0°C, and ice at 0°C is less dense

than liquid water at 0°C. Yes, ice will float on liquid water.

SECTION 15.2 HOMOGENOUS AQUEOUS SYSTEMS (pages 450–457)

This section describes the process of solvation; distinguishes among strong electrolytes, weak electrolytes, and nonelectrolytes; and explains water of hydration.

▶ Solvents and Solutes (page 450)

1. Water samples containing dissolved substances are called

_____aqueous solutions_____ .

CHAPTER 15, Water and Aqueous Systems *(continued)*

Match each term to its description by writing its letter on the line next to the description.

___c___ **2.** dissolving medium   **a.** solution

___b___ **3.** dissolved particles   **b.** solute

___a___ **4.** homogeneous mixture of particles in a   **c.** solvent
       dissolving medium

5. Is the following sentence true or false? After sodium chloride dissolves in a container of water, the sodium chloride will eventually settle to the bottom of the container if the solution remains undisturbed at a constant temperature.

_____ false _____

6. Circle the letter next to each sentence that is true about aqueous solutions.

    (**a.**) Solute particles can be either ionic or molecular, and their average diameters are usually less than 1 nanometer.

    (**b.**) When a solution is filtered, both solute and solvent will pass through the filter paper.

    (**c.**) Ionic compounds and substances containing polar covalent molecules readily dissolve in water.

    d. Nonpolar covalent molecules, such as those found in oil, grease, and gasoline, readily dissolve in water.

▶ The Solution Process (page 451)

7. What happens when a solid crystal of sodium chloride is placed in water?

Water molecules collide with the crystal and attract its Na^+ and Cl^- ions.

8. What process occurs when solute ions become surrounded by solvent molecules? _____ solvation _____

9. Look at the model of solvation in Figure 15.7 on page 451. If enough solvent is present, what will eventually happen to the ionic solid depicted at the bottom of the diagram?

All of the ions will become surrounded by solvent molecules and the ionic solid will

disappear into the solution.

10. When a compound cannot be solvated to any significant extent, it is called

_____ insoluble _____ .

11. Circle the letter next to the one sentence that best explains why the ionic compounds barium sulfate ($BaSO_4$) and calcium carbonate ($CaCO_3$) are nearly insoluble in water.

    a. The attractions between the ions in the crystals of these ionic compounds are weaker than the attractions between the ions and water molecules.

    b. The attractions between the ions in the crystals of these ionic compounds are stronger than the attractions between the ions and water molecules.

    c. There is no difference in the strength of the attractions between the ions in the crystals and the attractions between the ions and water molecules.

    d. These ionic compounds are easily dissolved in water.

12. What saying sums up the observation that, as a rule, polar solvents dissolve ionic compounds and polar molecules, but nonpolar solvents dissolve nonpolar compounds? ___"like dissolves like"___

▶ Electrolytes and Nonelectrolytes (pages 452–453)

13. What types of compounds can carry an electric current in the molten state or in aqueous solution? ___electrolytes___

14. Is the following sentence true or false? All ionic compounds are electrolytes. ___true___

15. Compounds that do not conduct an electric current in either aqueous solution or the molten state are called ___nonelectrolytes___ .

Look at the light bulbs in Figure 15.9 on page 453 to answer Questions 17, 18, and 19.

___c___ **16.** Which bulb, *a, b,* or *c,* indicates that the solution is nonconductive?

___b___ **17.** Which bulb, *a, b,* or *c,* indicates that the solution is weakly conductive?

___a___ **18.** Which bulb, *a, b,* or *c,* indicates that the solution is highly conductive?

▶ Hydrates (pages 454–457)

19. Water in a crystal that is an integral part of the crystal structure is called ___water of hydration___ .

20. A compound that contains water as an integral part of its crystal structure is called ___a hydrate___ .

21. What does "·$5H_2O$" mean when included in a chemical formula?
The compound contains five water molecules per formula unit.

CHAPTER 15, Water and Aqueous Systems *(continued)*

22. Circle the letter next to each sentence that is true about hydrated compounds. Use Figures 15.10 on page 454 to help you.

(a.) Crystals of copper sulfate pentahydrate always contain five molecules of water for each copper and sulfate ion pair.

(b.) Heating blue crystals of copper sulfate pentahydrate above 100°C drives off the water of hydration, leaving a white anhydrous powder.

(c.) It is possible to regenerate copper sulfate pentahydrate by treating anhydrous copper sulfate with water.

d. Anhydrous cobalt(II) chloride is a good indicator for the presence of water because it changes from pink to blue when exposed to moisture.

23. If a hydrate has a vapor pressure greater than that of the water in the surrounding air, the hydrate will lose water to the air, or _____ effloresce _____ .

24. Hygroscopic substances that remove water from the air are used as drying agents called _____ desiccants _____ .

25. Look at Figure 15.13 on page 457. What happens to dry sodium hydroxide pellets that are exposed to normally moist air? What kind of compound exhibits this behavior?

The sodium hydroxide pellets remove enough water from the air to dissolve

completely and form a solution. Sodium hydroxide is an example of a deliquescent

compound.

 # Reading Skill Practice

By looking carefully at photographs and drawings in your textbook, you can better understand what you have read. Look carefully at Figure 15.8 on page 451. What important idea does this photograph communicate? Do your work on a separate sheet of paper.

Students should recognize that oil spills cause environmental problems because the insoluble oil spreads out across the water. As it spreads, it can come into contact with plants and animals. Oil clogs pores and does other damage to the life cycle of living organisms.

SECTION 15.3 HETEROGENEOUS AQUEOUS SOLUTIONS (pages 459–462)

This section describes how colloids and suspensions differ from solutions and from one another. It also explains the Tyndall effect.

▶ Suspensions (page 459)

1. Is the following sentence true or false? Heterogeneous mixtures are not true solutions. _____true_____

2. Heterogeneous mixtures in which particles settle out upon standing are called _____suspensions_____ .

3. Is the following sentence true or false? When a suspension of clay particles in water is filtered, both clay and water will pass through the filter paper.
_____false_____

▶ Colloids (pages 460–462)

4. Heterogeneous mixtures in which particles are of intermediate size between those of true solutions and suspensions are called _____colloids_____ .

5. The scattering of light in all directions by colloidal particles is known as the _____Tyndall effect_____ .

6. Identify each type of system shown in the figure below.

| Solution | Colloid | Suspension |

CHAPTER 15, Water and Aqueous Systems *(continued)*

GUIDED PRACTICE PROBLEM

GUIDED PRACTICE PROBLEM 6 (page 456)

6. What is the percent by mass of water in $CuSO_4 \cdot 5H_2O$?

Analyze

a. What formula do you use to find percent by mass of water in a hydrate?

$$\text{percent } H_2O = \frac{\boxed{\text{mass of water}}}{\boxed{\text{mass of hydrate}}} \times \boxed{100\%}$$

b. From the periodic table, what is the average atomic mass of each of the following elements?

Cu = 63.5 g   O = 16.0 g

S = 32.1 g   H = 1.0 g

Calculate

c. Determine the mass of water in the hydrate.

$$\text{mass of } 5H_2O = 5 \times [(2 \times \boxed{1.0 \text{ g}}) + \boxed{16.0 \text{ g}}] = 5 \times \boxed{18.0 \text{ g}} = \boxed{90.0} \text{ g}$$

d. Determine the mass of the hydrate.

$$\text{mass of } CuSO_4{\cdot}5H_2O = 63.5 \text{ g} + 32.1 \text{ g} + (4 \times \boxed{16.0 \text{ g}}) + \boxed{90.0 \text{ g}} = \boxed{249.6} \text{ g}$$

e. Calculate the percent by mass of water.

$$\text{percent } H_2O = \frac{\boxed{90.0 \text{ g}}}{\boxed{249.6 \text{ g}}} \times 100\% = \boxed{36.1} \%$$

Evaluate

f. How do you know that your answer is correct?

Because the mass of water accounts for about a third of the total mass of the

hydrate, the percentage should be about 33%, which it is.

EXTRA PRACTICE (similar to Practice Problem 6, page 456)

6. What is the percent by mass of water in $CaCl_2{\cdot}2H_2O$?

mass of water = $2 \times [(2 \times 1.0) + 16.0] = 36.0$ g

mass of hydrate = $40.1 + (2 \times 35.5) + 36.0 = 147.1$ g

$$\text{percent water} = \frac{36.0 \text{ g}}{147.1 \text{ g}} \times 100\% = 24.5\%$$

16 SOLUTIONS

SECTION 16.1 PROPERTIES OF SOLUTIONS (pages 471–477)

This section identifies the factors that affect the solubility of a substance and determine the rate at which a solute dissolves.

▶ **Solution Formation** (pages 471–472)

Look at Figure 16.1 on page 471 to help you answer Questions 1 and 2.

1. Underline the condition that causes sugar to dissolve *faster* in water.

   a. as a whole cube   or   in <u>granulated form</u>?

   b. when allowed to stand   or   <u>when stirred</u>?

   c. at a <u>higher temperature</u>   or   a lower temperature?

2. Name three factors that influence the rate at which a solute dissolves in a solvent.

   a. _____ agitation (stirring or shaking) _____

   b. _____ temperature _____

   c. _____ particle size _____

3. Is the following sentence true or false? Finely ground particles dissolve more rapidly than larger particles because finer particles expose a greater surface area to the colliding solvent molecules. _____ true _____

▶ **Solubility** (pages 472–473)

4. Complete the following table showing the steps in a procedure to determine the total amount of sodium chloride that will dissolve in 100 g of water at 25°C.

Procedure	Amount Dissolved	Amount Not Dissolved
Add 36.0 g of sodium chloride to the water	36.0 g	0.0 g
Add an additional 1.0 g of sodium chloride	0.2 g	0.8 g
Determine the total amount that dissolves	36.2 g	

5. The amount of a substance that dissolves in a given quantity of solvent at a constant temperature is called the substance's _____ solubility _____ at that temperature.

6. If a solution contains the *maximum* amount of solute for a given quantity of solvent at a constant temperature, it is called a(n) _____ saturated _____ solution.

CHAPTER 16, Solutions *(continued)*

7. Look at Figure 16.2 on page 472. Circle the letter of each sentence that is true about a saturated solution.

   (a.) The total amount of dissolved solute remains constant.

   (b.) The total mass of undissolved crystals remains constant.

   (c.) When the rate of solvation equals the rate of crystallization, a state of dynamic equilibrium exists.

   d. If more solute were added to the container, the total amount of dissolved solute would increase.

8. If two liquids dissolve each other, they are said to be _____miscible_____ .

9. Look at Figure 16.3 on page 473. Why does the oil float on the vinegar?

   Vinegar is water-based, and oil and water are immiscible. The less dense oil floats

   on the water-based solution.

▶ Factors Affecting Solubility (pages 474–477)

10. Is the following sentence true or false? The solubility of sodium chloride in

    water increases to 39.2 g per 100 g of water at 100°C from 36.2 g per 100 g of

    water at 25°C. _____true_____

11. Circle the letter of the sentence that best answers the following question. How does the solubility of solid substances change as the temperature of the solvent increases?

    a. The solubility increases for all solids.

    (b.) The solubility increases for most solids.

    c. The solubility remains constant.

12. Look at Table 16.1 on page 474. Which solid substance listed in the table is

    nearly insoluble at any temperature? _____barium sulfate_____

13. How does the solubility of a gas change with an increase in temperature?

    As the temperature increases, the solubility of a gas decreases.

14. The directly proportional relationship between the solubility of a gas in a

    liquid and the pressure of the gas above the liquid is known as

    _____Henry's law_____ .

15. Describe the two diagrams of a bottled carbonated beverage below as *greater pressure* or *lower pressure,* and then as *greater solubility* or *lower solubility.* How do these two examples illustrate the relationship between the solubility of a gas and its vapor pressure?

In the closed bottle, the pressure is high and lots of CO_2 is dissolved in the

carbonated beverage. Once the cap is removed, the vapor pressure decreases,

allowing more CO_2 in the carbonated beverage to escape.

greater pressure and greater solubility   lower pressure and lower solubility

16. How does a solution become supersaturated? If the temperature of a solution having

a small excess of solid solute is raised, the solute dissolves. If the solution is then

allowed to cool slowly, the excess solute may stay dissolved at a temperature below

the temperature at which it would ordinarily crystallize.

SECTION 16.2 CONCENTRATIONS OF SOLUTIONS (pages 480–486)

This section explains how to solve problems involving molarity of a solution, how to prepare dilute solutions from more concentrated solutions, and what is meant by percent by volume and percent by mass.

▶ Molarity (pages 480–482)

1. A measure of the amount of solute dissolved in a given quantity of solvent is

the _____concentration_____ of a solution.

2. The most important unit of concentration in chemistry is _____molarity_____ .

3. Is the following sentence true or false? Molarity is the number of moles of

dissolved solute per liter of solvent. _____false_____

CHAPTER 16, Solutions *(continued)*

4. Look at Figure 16.8 on page 481. Circle the letter of the best procedure for making a 0.50-molar (0.50*M*) solution in a 1.0-L volumetric flask.

   a. Add distilled water exactly to the 1.0-L mark, add 0.50 mol of solute, and then agitate to dissolve the solute.

   b. Place 0.50 mol of solute in the flask, add distilled water to the 1.0-L mark, and then agitate to dissolve the solute.

   c. Combine 0.50 mol of water with 0.50 mol of solute in the flask, and then agitate to dissolve the solute.

   (d.) Fill the flask with distilled water until it is about half full, add 0.50 mol of solute, agitate to dissolve the solute, and then carefully fill the flask with distilled water to the 1.0-L mark.

5. List the information needed to find the molarity of a 2.0-L solution containing 0.50 mol of sodium chloride.

Known	**Unknown**
⎡ 2.0 liters ⎤ of solution	Molarity = ?
⎡ 0.50 mol ⎤ of sodium chloride	

$$\text{molarity } (M) = \frac{\boxed{\text{moles of solute}}}{\text{liters of solution}}$$

▶ Making Dilutions (pages 483–484)

6. How do you make a solution less concentrated? _____ Dilute it with solvent. _____

7. On the diagram below, assume that each beaker contains an equal number of moles of solute. Label each solution as *concentrated* or *dilute*. Then indicate the approximate relative volumes of each solution by drawing in the surface level on each beaker.

● Solute particle
● Solvent particle

Dilute	Concentrated

Questions 8 and 9 refer to the following situation. Solvent is added to a solution until the total volume of the solution doubles.

8. What happens to the number of moles of solute present in the solution when the volume doubles?

The number of moles of solute remains constant.

9. Circle the letter of the correct description of the change in molarity of a solution when the volume doubles.

a. The molarity of the solution is cut in half.

b. The molarity of the solution doubles.

c. The molarity of the solution remains constant.

d. The molarity of the solution increases slightly.

10. List the information you need to find how many milliliters of a stock solution of $2.00M$ $MgSO_4$ you would need to prepare 100.0 mL of $1.00M$ $MgSO_4$.

	Known	**Unknown**
$M_1 =$	2.00M	$V_1 = $? mL of $2.00M$ $MgSO_4$
$M_2 =$	1.00M	
$V_2 =$	100.0 mL	
$M_1 \times$	V_1	$= M_2 \times V_2$

▶ **Percent Solutions (pages 485–486)**

11. List the information needed to find the percent by volume of ethanol in a solution when 50 mL of pure ethanol is diluted with water to a volume of 250 mL.

Known		**Unknown**
Volume of ethanol $=$	50 mL	% ethanol by volume $= $? %
Volume of solution $=$	250 mL	

$$\% \ (v/v) = \frac{\text{volume of solute}}{\text{volume of solution}} \times 100\%$$

 # Reading Skill Practice

Writing a summary can help you remember the information you have read. When you write a summary, include only the most important points. Write a summary of the information about percent solutions on pages 485–486. Your summary should be shorter than the text on which it is based. Do your work on a separate sheet of paper.

Student summaries should explain that if both the solvent and the solute are liquids, volumes of the solvent and the solution can be measured, and the concentration can be expressed as a percent by volume. If solids are dissolved in liquids, the masses of both the solvent and the solute must be obtained to express the concentration as a percent by mass.

CHAPTER 16, Solutions *(continued)*

SECTION 16.3 COLLIGATIVE PROPERTIES OF SOLUTIONS (pages 487–490)

This section explains why a solution has a lower vapor pressure, an elevated boiling point, and a depressed freezing point compared with the pure solvent of that solution.

▶ **Vapor Pressure Lowering** (pages 487–488)

1. Properties of a solution that depend only on the number of particles dissolved, but not the identity of solute particles in the solution are called
   _____colligative properties_____ .

2. Is the following sentence true or false? A nonvolatile substance is one that does not vaporize easily. _____true_____

3. Look at Figure 16.13 on page 487. What happens to the vapor pressure equilibrium when a nonvolatile solute is added to a pure solvent?
   The equilibrium is disturbed as solvent particles form shells around solute particles.
   Equilibrium is eventually re-established at a lower vapor pressure.

4. How is the decrease in vapor pressure of a solution with a nonvolatile solute related to the number of particles per formula unit of solute?
   The decrease in vapor pressure is proportional to the number of particles the solute
   produces in solution. Solutes with more particles per formula unit produce a larger
   decrease in vapor pressure.

5. Assume 3 mol each of three different solutes have been added to three identical beakers of water as shown below. If the beakers are covered to form closed systems at constant temperature, rank the vapor pressures in each container from 1 (lowest) to 3 (highest).

| 3 | 2 | 1 |

 Glucose Na^+ ○ Cl^- ● Ca^{2+}

▶ **Freezing-Point Depression** (pages 488–489)

6. Circle the letter of each sentence that is true about the freezing point of a solution formed by a liquid solvent and nonvolatile solute.

   a. When a substance freezes, the arrangement of its particles becomes less orderly.

   b. The presence of a solute in water disrupts the formation of orderly patterns as the solution is cooled to the freezing point of pure water.

   c. More kinetic energy must be withdrawn from a solution than from a pure solvent in order for the solution to solidify.

   d. The freezing point of the solution is lower than the freezing point of the pure solvent.

7. One mole of which substance, glucose or sodium chloride, will produce more freezing-point depression when added to equal amounts of water? Why?

   Sodium chloride because it produces twice as many particles per formula unit in

   solution than glucose.

▶ **Boiling-Point Elevation** (page 490)

8. Circle the letter next to each sentence that is true concerning the boiling point of a solution formed by a liquid solvent and a nonvolatile solute.

   a. The boiling point is the temperature at which the vapor pressure equals atmospheric pressure.

   b. Adding a nonvolatile solute decreases the vapor pressure.

   c. Because of the decrease in vapor pressure, additional kinetic energy must be added to raise the vapor pressure of the liquid phase to atmospheric pressure.

   d. The boiling point of the solution is higher than the boiling point of the pure solvent.

9. The difference between the boiling point of a solution and that of the pure solvent is called the _____ boiling-point elevation _____ .

SECTION 16.4 CALCULATIONS INVOLVING COLLIGATIVE PROPERTIES (pages 491–496)

This section explains how to calculate the molality and mole fraction of a solution, and how to use molality to calculate the freezing-point depression or boiling-point elevation of a solution.

▶ **Molality and Mole Fraction** (pages 491–493)

1. For a solution, the ratio of moles of solute to mass of solvent in kilograms, represented by m, is the solution's _____ molality _____ .

CHAPTER 16, Solutions *(continued)*

2. Is the following sentence true or false? Molarity and molality are always the same for a solution. _____ false _____

3. What is the molality of a solution prepared by adding 1.0 mol of sodium chloride to 2.0 kg of water? _____ 0.50*m* _____

4. The circle graph below shows the ratio of ethylene glycol (EG) to water in one antifreeze solution. Write the mole fractions for each substance.

Mole fraction EG $= \dfrac{\boxed{1.50}}{\boxed{1.50} + \boxed{4.80}} = \dfrac{\boxed{1.50 \cdot}}{\boxed{6.30}} = \boxed{0.240}$

Mole fraction $H_2O = \dfrac{\boxed{4.80}}{\boxed{1.50} + \boxed{4.80}} = \dfrac{\boxed{4.80}}{\boxed{6.30}} = \boxed{0.760}$

1.50 mol
EG

4.80 mol
H_2O

▶ Freezing-Point Depression and Boiling-Point Elevation (pages 494–496)

5. Assuming a solute is molecular and not ionic, the magnitude of the boiling-point elevation of the solution, ΔT_b, is directly proportional to

   the molal concentration of the solute (*m*) _____ .

6. Look at Table 16.3 on page 495. What is the molal boiling-point elevation constant, K_b, for water? _____ 0.512°C/*m* _____

7. You need to find the freezing point of a 1.50*m* aqueous NaCl solution. You calculate ΔT_f to be 1.86°C/*m* × 3.00*m* or 5.86°C. What is the temperature at which the solution freezes? _____ −5.86°C _____

GUIDED PRACTICE PROBLEMS

GUIDED PRACTICE PROBLEM 1 (page 477)

1. The solubility of a gas in water is 0.16 g/L at 104 kPa of pressure. What is the solubility when the pressure of the gas is increased to 288 kPa? Assume the temperature remains constant.

Analyze

Step 1. What is the equation for the relationship between solubility and

pressure? $\dfrac{S_1}{P_1} = \dfrac{S_2}{P_2}$

Step 2. What is this law called? _____Henry's law_____

Step 3. What are the known values in this problem?

$P_1 = $ | 104 kPa |

$S_1 = $ | 0.16 g/L |

| P_2 | $= 288$ kPa

Step 4. What is the unknown in this problem? _____S_2_____

Solve

Step 5. Rearrange the equation to solve for the unknown.

$S_2 = \left| \dfrac{S_1 \times P_2}{P_1} \right|$

Step 6. Substitute the known values into the equation and solve.

$S_2 = \dfrac{\boxed{0.16}\ \text{g/L} \times \boxed{288}\ \cancel{\text{kPa}}}{\boxed{104}\ \cancel{\text{kPa}}} = \boxed{0.44\ \text{g/L}}$

Evaluate

Step 7. How do you know that your answer is correct?

The pressure increased nearly threefold, so the solubility should increase nearly

threefold, which it does.

Step 8. Are the units correct? Explain.

Yes, because solubility is expressed as grams of gas dissolved per liter of solution.

_____

CHAPTER 16, Solutions *(continued)*

GUIDED PRACTICE PROBLEM 8 (page 481)

8. A solution has a volume of 2.0 L and contains 36.0 g of glucose. If the molar mass of glucose is 180 g/mol, what is the molarity of the solution?

Step 1. What is the equation for molarity of a solution?

$$\text{Molarity } (M) = \frac{\text{moles of solute}}{\text{liters of solution}}$$

Step 2. How many moles of glucose are in the solution?

$$\boxed{36.0} \ \text{g} \times \frac{1 \ \text{mol}}{\boxed{180} \ \text{g}} = \boxed{0.20} \ \text{mol glucose}$$

Step 3. Substitute the known values into the equation for molarity.

$$M = \frac{\boxed{0.20 \ \text{mol}}}{2.0 \ \boxed{L}}$$

Step 4. Solve.

$$M = \underline{\hspace{1cm} 0.10 \ \text{mol/L} \hspace{1cm}}$$

GUIDED PRACTICE PROBLEM 9 (page 481)

9. A solution has a volume of 250 mL and contains 0.70 mol NaCl. What is its molarity?

Analyze

Step 1. List the knowns and the unknown.

Knowns

number of moles of solute = 0.70 mol NaCl

solution volume = 250 mL = 0.250 L

Unknown

solution concentration (molarity) = ? M

The units of molarity, M, is mol solute/L solution.

Calculate

Step 2. Solve for the unknown.
As long as the units are correct, division gives the result.

$$\text{molarity} = \frac{\text{mol solute}}{\text{solution volume}} = \frac{0.70 \ \text{mol NaCl}}{0.250 \ \text{L}}$$

$$= \underline{\hspace{1cm} 2.8 \ M \hspace{1cm}}$$

Evaluate

Step 3. Does the result make sense?

The numerical answer should be 4 times greater than the number of moles of

solute, because 250 mL is one-fourth of 1 L.

EXTRA PRACTICE (similar to Practice Problem 10, page 482)

10. How many moles of ammonium nitrate are in 375 mL of $0.40M$ NH_4NO_3?

$$375 \text{ mL} \times \frac{0.40 \text{ mol}}{1 \text{ L}} \times \frac{1 \text{ L}}{1000 \text{ mL}} = 0.15 \text{ mol}$$

GUIDED PRACTICE PROBLEM 12 (page 484)

12. How many milliliters of a solution of $4.00M$ KI is needed to prepare 250.0 mL of $0.760M$ KI?

Analyze

Step 1. List the knowns and the unknown.

Knowns

$M_1 = 4.00M$ KI

M_2 5 $0.760M$ KI

$V_2 = 250.0$ mL

$M_1 \times V_1 = M_2 \times V_2$

Unknown

$V_1 = ?$ mL of $4.00M$ KI

Calculate

Step 2. Solve for the unknown.
Rearranging the equation above will give the result

$$V_1 = \frac{M_2 \times V_2}{M_1} = \frac{0.760M \text{ KI} \times 250.0 \text{ mL}}{4.00M \text{ KI}}$$

$$= \underline{\quad 47.5 \text{ mL of } 4.00M \text{ KI} \quad}$$

CHAPTER 16, Solutions *(continued)*

Step 3. Evaluate Does the result make sense?

The concentration of the initial solution is more than 5 times larger than that of the

final solution, so the volume of initial solution should be about one-fifth of the total

volume of the diluted solution.

GUIDED PRACTICE PROBLEM 14 (page 485)

14. If 10 mL of pure propanone (or acetone) is diluted with water to a total solution volume of 200 mL, what is the percent by volume of acetone in the solution?

Step 1. What is the equation for calculating percent by volume?

$$\% \ (v/v) = \frac{\text{volume of solute}}{\text{volume of solution}} \times 100\%$$

Step 2. What are the knowns in this problem?

volume of acetone = 10 mL

volume of solution = 200 mL

Step 3. Substitute the known values into the equation and solve.

$$\% \ (v/v) = \frac{\boxed{10} \ \text{mL}}{\boxed{200} \ \text{mL}} \times 100\% = \boxed{5} \ \%$$

GUIDED PRACTICE PROBLEM 29 (page 492)

29. How many grams of sodium fluoride are needed to prepare a 0.400*m* NaF solution that contains 750 g of water?

Analyze

Step 1. List the knowns and the unknown.

Knowns

mass of water = 750 g

solution concentration = 0.400*m*

molar mass NaF = 42.0 g/mol

Unknown

mass of solute = ? g NaF

The final solution must contain 0.400 mol of NaF per 1000 g of water. This information will provide a conversion factor. The process of conversion will be: grams of water → mol NaF → grams NaF

Calculate

Step 2. Solve for the unknown.
Multiply by the appropriate conversion factors:

$$750 \text{ g H}_2\text{O} \times \frac{0.400 \text{ mol NaF}}{100 \text{ g H}_2\text{O}} \times \frac{42.0 \text{ g NaF}}{1 \text{ mol NaF}}$$

$$= \underline{\qquad 12.6 \text{ g NaF} \qquad}$$

Evaluate

Step 3. Does the result make sense?

A one molal NaF solution contains 42.0 g NaF. Given only three-fourths of 1000 g

of H_2O and less than half concentration, the result should be less than three-eighths

the molar mass.

EXTRA PRACTICE (similar to Practice Problem 31, page 493)

31. What is the mole fraction of each component in a solution made by mixing 230 g of ethanol (C_2H_5OH) and 450 g of water?

$$n_{\text{ETH}} = \underline{\qquad 230 \text{ g} \times \frac{1 \text{ mol}}{46.0 \text{ g}} = 5.0 \text{ mol} \qquad}$$

$$n_{\text{WAT}} = \underline{\qquad 450 \text{ g} \times \frac{1 \text{ mol}}{18.0 \text{ g}} = 25 \text{ mol} \qquad}$$

$$X_{\text{ETH}} = \underline{\qquad \frac{5.0 \text{ mol}}{5.0 \text{ mol} + 25 \text{ mol}} = 0.17 \qquad}$$

$$X_{\text{WAT}} = \underline{\qquad \frac{25 \text{ mol}}{5.0 \text{ mol} + 25 \text{ mol}} = 0.83 \qquad}$$

CHAPTER 16, Solutions *(continued)*

GUIDED PRACTICE PROBLEM 33 (page 495)

33. What is the freezing point depression of an aqueous solution of 10.0 g glucose ($C_6H_{12}O_6$) in 50.0 g H_2O?

Analyze

Step 1. List the knowns and the unknown.

Knowns

mass of solute = 10.0 g $C_6H_{12}O_6$

mass of solvent = 50.0 g H_2O = 0.0500 kg H_2O

K_f for water = 1.86°C/m

$\_T_f = K_f \times m$

Unknown

$\_T_f = ?°C$

To use the given equation, first convert the mass of solute to the number of moles, then calculate the molality, m.

Calculate

Step 2. Solve for the unknown.
Calculate the molar mass of $C_6H_{12}O_6$: 1mol $C_6H_{12}O_6$ = _____180 g_____

Calculate the number of moles of solute using this conversion:

$$\text{mol } C_6H_{12}O_6 = 10.0 \text{ g } C_6H_{12}O_6 \times \frac{1 \text{ mol } C_6H_{12}O_6}{180 \text{ g } C_6H_{12}O_6}$$

$$= \underline{\quad 0.0556 \text{ mol } C_6H_{12}O_6 \quad}$$

Calculate the molality:

$$m = \frac{\text{mol solute}}{\text{kg solvent}} = \frac{0.0556 \text{ mol } C_6H_{12}O_6}{0.0500 \text{ kg } H_2O}$$

$$= \underline{\quad 1.11m \quad}$$

Calculate the freezing point depression using the known formula:

$\_T_f = K_f \times m = 1.86°C/m \times 1.11 \ m = 2.06°C$

Evaluate

Step 3. Does the result make sense?

Because a one molal solution decreases the freezing point of water by 1.86°C, a

solution with concentration about one-tenth larger should decrease the freezing

point further by about one-tenth of K_f.

GUIDED PRACTICE PROBLEM 35 (page 496)

35. What is the boiling point of a solution that contains 1.25 mol $CaCl_2$ in 1400 g of water?

Step 1. What is the concentration of the $CaCl_2$ solution?

$$\frac{1.25 \text{ mol}}{\boxed{1400} \text{ g}} \times \frac{\boxed{1000} \text{ g}}{1 \text{ kg}} = \boxed{0.89} \, m$$

Step 2. How many particles are produced by the ionization of each formula unit of $CaCl_2$?

$CaCl_2(s) \longrightarrow Ca^+ + \boxed{2} \, Cl^-$,

therefore ___3___ particles are produced.

Step 3. What is the total molality of the solution?

___3___ × $0.89m = 2.7m$

Step 4. What is the molal boiling point elevation constant (K_b) for water?

K_b (water) = ___0.512___ °C/m

Step 5. Calculate the boiling point elevation.

ΔT_b = ___0.512___ °C/m × 2.7 ___m___

= 1.4 ___°C___

Step 6. Add ΔT_b to 100°C to find the new boiling point.

___1.4___ °C + 100°C = ___101.4___ °C

GUIDED PRACTICE PROBLEM 36 (page 496)

33. What mass of NaCl would have to be dissolved in 1.000 kg of water to raise the boiling point by 2.00°C?

Analyze

Step 1. List the knowns and the unknown.

CHAPTER 16, Solutions *(continued)*

Knowns

mass of solvent = 1.000 kg H_2O

K_f for water = 1.86°C/m

_T_b = 2.00°C

_T_b = $K_b \times m$

Unknown

mass of solute = 10.0 g NaCl

First calculate the molality, m, using the given equation. Then use a molar mass conversion to determine the mass of solute.

Calculate

Step 2. Solve for the unknown.
Calculate the molality by rearranging _T_b = $K_b \times m$:

$$m = \_T_b/K_b = \frac{2.00°C}{1.86°C/m}$$

= ____1.08m____

Calculate the molar mass of NaCl: 1 mol NaCl = 58.5 g

= ___5.85×10^{-2}___ kg NaCl

Determine the number of moles of solute using the molality and the amount of solvent:

moles NaCl = mass of solvent × molality = 1.000 kg H_2O × $\dfrac{1.08 \text{ mol NaCl}}{1 \text{ kg } H_2O}$

= ____1.08 mol NaCl____

Finally, convert the number of moles of NaCl to mass:

1.08 mol NaCl × $\dfrac{5.85 \times 10^{-2} \text{ kg NaCl}}{1 \text{ mol NaCl}}$

= ___6.32×10^{-2} kg NaCl___

Evaluate

Step 3. Does the result make sense?

Because the solution's molality is slightly more than one, the mass of solute

should be slightly more than one times the numerical value of molar mass.

17 THERMOCHEMISTRY

SECTION 17.1 THE FLOW OF ENERGY—HEAT AND WORK (pages 505–510)

This section explains the relationship between energy and heat, and distinguishes between heat capacity and specific heat.

▶ Energy Transformations (page 505)

1. What area of study in chemistry is concerned with the heat transfers that occur during chemical reactions? ___thermochemistry___

2. Where the use of energy is concerned (in a scientific sense), when is work done?
   Work is done when a force is used to move an object.

3. Circle the letter next to each sentence that is true about energy.

   (a.) Energy is the capacity for doing work or supplying heat.

   (b.) Energy is detected only because of its effects.

   c. Heat is energy that transfers from one object to another because they are at the same temperature.

   (d.) Gasoline contains a significant amount of chemical potential energy.

4. Circle the letter next to each sentence that is true about heat.

   (a.) One effect of adding heat to a substance is an increase in the temperature of that substance.

   b. Heat always flows from a cooler object to a warmer object.

   (c.) If two objects remain in contact, heat will flow from the warmer object to the cooler object until the temperature of both objects is the same.

▶ Exothermic and Endothermic Processes (pages 506–507)

5. What can be considered the "system" and what are the "surroundings" when studying a mixture of chemicals undergoing a reaction? Write your answers where indicated below.

   System: The mixture of chemicals itself is considered the system.

   _____

   Surroundings: Everything but the mixture of chemicals is the surroundings, but

   practically speaking, the immediate vicinity of the system.

CHAPTER 17, Thermochemistry *(continued)*

6. In thermochemical calculations, is the direction of heat flow given from the point of view of the system, or of the surroundings?

The direction is given from the point of view of the system.

7. What universal law states that energy can neither be created nor destroyed and can always be accounted for as work, stored potential energy, or heat?

the law of conservation of energy

Questions 8 through 12 refer to the systems and surroundings illustrated in diagrams (a) and (b) below.

(a) **(b)**

8. Which diagram illustrates an endothermic process? _____ *b*

9. Is heat flow positive or negative in diagram (a)? _____ *negative*

10. Which diagram illustrates an exothermic process? _____ *a*

11. Is heat flow positive or negative in diagram (b)? _____ *positive*

12. What does a negative value for heat represent?

It shows that a system is losing heat.

To answer Questions 13 and 14, look at Figure 17.2 on page 506.

13. A system is a person sitting next to a campfire. Is this system endothermic or exothermic? Explain why.

The system is endothermic because the system is absorbing heat from the campfire.

14. A system is a person who is perspiring. Is this system endothermic or exothermic? Explain why.

The system is exothermic because the system is cooling off by producing perspiration,

which will evaporate, cooling the system.

Name _____ Date _____ Class _____

▶ Units for Measuring Heat Flow (page 507)

15. Heat generated by the human body is usually measured in units called
_____calories_____ .

16. Describe the chemical reaction that generates heat in the human body.

The body breaks down sugars and fats into carbon dioxide and water.

17. What is the definition of a calorie?

A calorie is defined as the quantity of heat needed to raise the temperature of 1 g of

pure water 1°C.

18. How is the calorie (written with a lower case c) related to the dietary Calorie (written with a capital C)?

One dietary Calorie is equal to 1000 calories or 1 kilocalorie.

19. Circle the letter next to the SI unit of heat and energy.

a. calorie

b. Calorie

c. joule

d. Celsius degree

▶ Heat Capacity and Specific Heat (pages 508–510)

20. Is the next sentence true or false? Samples of two different substances having

the same mass always have the same heat capacity. _____false_____

21. Compare the heat capacity of a 2-kg steel frying pan and a 2-g steel pin. If the heat capacities of these objects differ, explain why.

The frying pan has a greater heat capacity because its mass is greater.

22. Is the next sentence true or false? The specific heat of a substance varies with

the mass of the sample. _____false_____

SECTION 17.2 MEASURING AND EXPRESSING ENTHALPY CHANGES (pages 511–517)

This section explains how to construct equations and perform calculations that show enthalpy changes for chemical and physical processes.

▶ Calorimetry (pages 511–513)

1. The property that is useful for keeping track of heat transfers in chemical

and physical processes at constant pressure is called _____enthalpy_____ .

CHAPTER 17, Thermochemistry *(continued)*

2. What is calorimetry? ___Calorimetry is the accurate and precise measurement of___

___heat change for chemical and physical processes.___

3. Use Figure 17.5 on page 511. Circle the letter next to each sentence that is true about calorimeters.

(a.) The calorimeter container is insulated to minimize loss of heat to or absorption of heat from the surroundings.

(b.) Because foam cups are excellent heat insulators, they may be used as simple calorimeters.

c. A stirrer is used to keep temperatures uneven in a calorimeter.

(d.) In the calorimeter shown in Figure 17.5, the chemical substances dissolved in water constitute the system and the water is part of the surroundings.

4. Is the following sentence true or false? For systems at constant pressure, heat flow and enthalpy change are the same thing. _____true_____

5. Complete the table below to show the direction of heat flow and type of reaction for positive and negative change of enthalpy.

Sign of Enthalpy Change	Direction of Heat Flow	Is Reaction Endothermic or Exothermic?
ΔH is positive ($\Delta H > 0$)	into system	endothermic
ΔH is negative ($\Delta H < 0$)	out of system	exothermic

6. Name each quantity that is represented in the equation for heat change in an aqueous solution.

$$q \quad = \quad \Delta H \quad = \quad m \quad \times \quad C \quad \times \quad \Delta T$$

| heat flow | enthalpy | mass of the water | specific heat of water | change in temperature |

▶ Thermochemical Equations (pages 514–517)

7. What happens to the temperature of water after calcium oxide is added?

The temperature increases.

8. A chemical equation that includes the heat change is called a ___thermochemical___ equation.

9. Why is it important to give the physical state of the reactants and products in a thermochemical equation?

The heat change values differ when the products or reactants are in different states.

10. Complete the enthalpy diagram for the combustion of natural gas. Use the thermochemical equation in the first paragraph on page 517 as a guide.

SECTION 17.3 HEAT IN CHANGES OF STATE (pages 520–526)

This section explains heat transfers that occur during melting, freezing, boiling, and condensing.

▶ Heats of Fusion and Solidification (pages 520–521)

1. Is the following sentence true or false? A piece of ice placed in a bowl in a warm room will remain at a temperature of 0°C until all of the ice has melted.

_____ true _____

2. Circle the letter next to each sentence that is true about heat of fusion and heat of solidification of a given substance.

   (a.) The molar heat of fusion is the negative of the molar heat of solidification.

   b. Heat is released during melting and absorbed during freezing.

   (c.) Heat is absorbed during melting and released during freezing.

   (d.) The quantity of heat absorbed during melting is exactly the same as the quantity of heat released when the liquid solidifies.

3. Use Table 17.3 on page 522. Determine ΔH for each of these physical changes.

   a. $H_2(s) \longrightarrow H_2(l)$ $\Delta H =$ _____ 0.12 kJ/mol _____

   b. $Ne(s) \longrightarrow Ne(l)$ $\Delta H =$ _____ 0.33 kJ/mol _____

   c. $O_2(s) \longrightarrow O_2(l)$ $\Delta H =$ _____ 0.44 kJ/mol _____

▶ Heats of Vaporization and Condensation (pages 522–524)

4. Is the following sentence true or false? As liquids absorb heat at their boiling points, the temperature remains constant while they vaporize.

_____ true _____

CHAPTER 17, Thermochemistry *(continued)*

Use the heating curve for water shown below to answer Questions 5, 6, and 7.

Heating Curve for Water

5. Label the melting point and boiling point temperatures on the graph.

6. What happens to the temperature during melting and vaporization?

   The temperature stays constant at the melting point and boiling point, respectively.

   _____

7. Circle the letter next to the process that *releases* the most heat.

   a. Melting of 1 mol of water at 0°C

   b. Freezing of 1 mol of water at 0°C

   c. Vaporization of 1 mol of water at 100°C

   d. Condensation of 1 mol of water at 100°C

Look at Table 17.3 on page 522 to help you answer Questions 8 and 9.

8. How many of the 6 substances listed have a higher molar heat of vaporization

   than water? Which one(s)? _____1; ethanol_____

9. It takes _____3.16 kJ_____ of energy to convert 1 mol of methanol molecules
   in the solid state to 1 mol of methanol molecules in the liquid state at the
   normal melting point.

▶ **Heat of Solution** (pages 525–526)

10. The heat change caused by dissolution of one mole of a substance is the

_____ molar heat of solution _____.

11. How does a cold pack containing water and ammonium nitrate work?

When activated, the cold pack allows water and ammonium nitrate to mix, producing

an endothermic reaction. As heat is absorbed in the reaction, the temperature of the

pack falls.

 Reading Skill Practice

Writing a summary can help you remember the information you have read. When you write a summary, write only the most important points. Write a summary for each of the five types of heat changes described on pages 520–526. Your summary should be much shorter than these six pages of text. Do your work on another sheet of paper.

Students should describe briefly heat of fusion and solidification, heat of vaporization and condensation, and heat of solution.

SECTION 17.4 CALCULATING HEATS OF REACTION (pages 527–532)

This section explains how Hess's law of heat summation and standard heats of formation may be applied to find enthalpy changes for a series of chemical and physical processes.

▶ **Hess's Law** (pages 527–529)

1. For reactions that occur in a series of steps, Hess's law of heat summation says that if you add the thermochemical equations for each step to give a final equation for the reaction, you may also _____

add the heats of reaction for each step to give the final heat of reaction _____ .

2. Is the following sentence true or false? Graphite is a more stable form of elemental carbon than diamond at 25°C, so diamond will slowly change to graphite over an extremely long period of time. _____ true

3. Look at Figures 17.13 and 17.14 on pages 528 and 529. According to Hess's law, the enthalpy change from diamond to carbon dioxide can be expressed as the sum of what three enthalpy changes?

a. _____ diamond to graphite (−1.9 kJ) _____

b. _____ graphite to carbon monoxide (−110.5 kJ) _____

c. _____ carbon monoxide to carbon dioxide (−283.0 kJ) _____

CHAPTER 17, Thermochemistry *(continued)*

▶ Standard Heats of Formation (pages 530–532)

4. The change in enthalpy that accompanies the formation of one mole of a
   compound from its elements with all substances in their standard states at
   25°C and 101.3 kPa is called the _____standard heat of formation_____ .

5. Is the following sentence true or false? Chemists have set the standard
   heat of formation of free elements, including elements that occur in
   nature as diatomic molecules, at zero. _____true_____

6. Complete the enthalpy diagram below by finding the heat of formation when
   hydrogen and oxygen gases combine to form hydrogen peroxide at 25°C. Use
   the data in Table 17.4 on page 530 and the equation $\Delta H^0 = \Delta H_f^0$ (products) $-$
   ΔH_f^0 (reactants) to find the answer.

7. Look at Table 17.4. Methane burns to form carbon dioxide and water vapor.

   $$CH_4(g) + 2O_2(g) \longrightarrow CO_2(g) + 2H_2O(g)$$

   a. Will the heat of this reaction be positive or negative? How do you know?

      It will be negative; the heats of formation for carbon dioxide and water vapor

      are much less than zero. The heat of formation of methane is much closer to zero.

      _____

   b. How does your experience confirm that your answer to Question 7a is
      reasonable?

      The burning of fuels such as methane gives off heat. Exothermic reactions have

      negative heats of reaction.

GUIDED PRACTICE PROBLEMS

GUIDED PRACTICE PROBLEM 3 (page 510)

3. When 435 J of heat is added to 3.4 g of olive oil at 21°C, the temperature increases to 85°C. What is the specific heat of the olive oil?

Analyze

a. What is the formula for calculating specific heat? $C = \dfrac{q}{m \times \Delta T}$

b. What are the knowns and the unknown in this problem?

Knowns: Unknown:

$m = $ ___3.4 g___ $C_{olive\ oil}$

$q = $ ___435 J___

$\Delta T = $ ___(85°C − 21°C) = 64°C___

Calculate

c. Substitute the known values into the equation for specific heat and solve.

$$C_{olive\ oil} = \boxed{\dfrac{435\ J}{3.4\ g \times 64°C}} = 2.0 \boxed{J/(g{\cdot}°C)}$$

Evaluate

d. Explain why you think your answer is reasonable. Think about the time it takes to fry foods in olive oil versus the time it takes to cook foods in boiling water.

Because the specific heat of olive oil is lower than the specific heat of water, olive

oil can reach a higher temperature than water when the same amount of energy

is added to equal masses of each. This property makes olive oil good for cooking

foods quickly because olive oil heats up more quickly than water under the same

conditions.

e. Are the units in your answer correct? How do you know?

Yes, because specific heat is expressed in J/(g•°C), or cal/(g•°C).

CHAPTER 17, Thermochemistry *(continued)*

GUIDED PRACTICE PROBLEM 12 (page 513)

12. When 50.0 mL of water containing 0.50 mol HCl at 22.5°C is mixed with 50.0 mL of water containing 0.50 mol NaOH at 22.5°C in a calorimeter, the temperature of the solution increased to 26.0°C. How much heat (in kJ) was released by this reaction?

a. Calculate the final volume of the water. V_{final} = 50.0 mL + 50.0 mL = <u>100.0 mL</u>

b. Calculate the total mass of the water, using the density of water. m = <u>100.0</u> mL × $\dfrac{\boxed{1.00}\ g}{mL}$ = <u>100. g</u>

c. Calculate ΔT. ΔT = 26.0 °C − <u>22.5</u> °C = <u>3.5</u> °C

d. Substitute the known quantities into the equation for changes in enthalpy (ΔH). ΔH = (<u>100.</u> g) × (4.18 <u>J/(g•°C)</u>)
  × <u>3.5</u> °C

e. Solve. <u>1500</u> J

f. Convert joules to kilojoules (kJ) and round to three significant figures. <u>1500</u> J × $\dfrac{1\ kJ}{1000\ J}$ = <u>1.5</u> kJ

EXTRA PRACTICE (similar to Practice Problem 14, page 516)

14. When carbon disulfide is formed from its elements, heat is absorbed. Calculate the amount of heat (in kJ) absorbed when 8.53 g of carbon disulfide is formed.

$$C(s) + 2S(s) \longrightarrow CS_2(l) \qquad \Delta H = 89.3\ kJ$$

$$8.53\ \cancel{g\ CS_2} \times \frac{89.3\ kJ}{1\ \cancel{mol\ CS_2}} \times \frac{1\ \cancel{mol\ CS_2}}{76.2\ \cancel{g\ CS_2}} = 10.0\ kJ$$

GUIDED PRACTICE PROBLEM 22 (page 521)

22. How many grams of ice at 0°C could be melted by the addition of 0.400 kJ of heat?

a. Write the conversion factors from ΔH_{fus} and the molar mass of ice. $\dfrac{1\ mol\ ice}{\boxed{6.01}\ kJ}$ and $\dfrac{\boxed{18.0}\ g\ ice}{1\ mol\ ice}$

b. Multiply the known heat change by the conversion factors. 0.400 $\cancel{kJ}$ × $\dfrac{1\ \cancel{mol\ ice}}{\boxed{6.01}\ \cancel{kJ}}$ × $\dfrac{\boxed{18.0}\ g\ ice}{1\ \cancel{mol\ ice}}$
  = $\boxed{1.20}$ g ice

EXTRA PRACTICE (similar to Practice Problem 23, page 524)

23. How much heat (in kJ) is absorbed when 88.45 g $H_2O(l)$ at 100°C and 101.3 kPa is converted to steam at 100°C? Express your answer in kJ.

$$88.45\ \cancel{g\ H_2O} \times \frac{1\ \cancel{mol\ H_2O}}{18.0\ \cancel{g\ H_2O}} \times \frac{40.7\ kJ}{1\ \cancel{mol\ H_2O}} = 200\ kJ$$

| 18 | # REACTION RATES AND EQUILIBRIUM |

SECTION 18.1 RATES OF REACTION (pages 541–547)

This section explains what is meant by the rate of a chemical reaction. It also uses collision theory to show how the rate of a chemical reaction is influenced by the reaction conditions.

▶ **Collision Theory** (pages 541–544)

1. How are rates of chemical change expressed?

   Rates of chemical change are usually expressed as the amount of reactant changing
   per unit time.

2. Look at Figure 18.3 on page 542. In a typical reaction, as time passes, the

   amount of _____ reactant _____ decreases and the amount of

   _____ product _____ increases.

3. What does collision theory say about the energies of atoms, ions, or molecules reacting to form products when they collide?

   Collision theory states that the particles must have enough kinetic energy when they
   collide to form products.

   _____

4. Look at the figures below. One shows a collision that results in the formation of product. Label it *effective collision*. Label the other collision *ineffective collision*.

   _____ ineffective collision _____   _____ effective collision _____

5. Is the following sentence true or false? Particles lacking the necessary kinetic

   energy to react bounce apart unchanged when they collide. _____ true _____

6. Look at Figure 18.5 on page 543. Which arrangement of atoms contains the least amount of energy?

   a. reactants

   b. activated complex

   c. products

CHAPTER 18, Reaction Rates and Equilibrium *(continued)*

7. Circle the letter of the term that completes the sentence correctly. The minimum amount of energy that particles must have in order to react is called the _____ .

a. kinetic energy   **c.** potential energy

(b.) activation energy   **d.** collision energy

8. An activated complex is the arrangement of atoms at the _____peak_____ of the activation-energy barrier.

9. Circle the letter of the term that best describes the lifetime of an activated complex.

a. 10^{-15} s   **b.** 10^{13} s   **(c.)** 10^{-13} s   **d.** 10^{-1} s

10. Why is an activated complex sometimes called the transition state?

It is called the transition state because an activated complex is unstable and is as

likely to re-form reactants as it is to form products.

▶ Factors Affecting Reaction Rates *(pages 545–547)*

11. Changes in the rate of chemical reactions depend on conditions such as
temperature, concentration, and particle size .

12. The main effect of increasing the temperature of a chemical reaction is to
_____increase_____ the number of particles that have enough kinetic energy
to react when they collide.

13. What happens when you put more reacting particles into a fixed volume?

The concentration of reactants increases, the collision frequency increases, and,

therefore, the reaction rate increases.

14. Is the following sentence true or false? The smaller the particle size, the larger
the surface area of a given mass of particles. _____true_____

15. What are some ways to increase the surface area of solid reactants?

One way is to dissolve the solid; another way is to grind the solid into a fine powder.

16. A _____catalyst_____ is a substance that increases the rate of a reaction
without being used up itself during the reaction.

17. What does a catalyst do? A catalyst permits reactions to proceed at a lower energy

than is normally required. A catalyst lowers the activation energy.

The graph below shows the reaction rate of the same reaction with and without a catalyst. Use it to help you answer Questions 18 and 19.

18. Label each curve as *with catalyst* or *without catalyst*.

19. What does the graph show about the effect of a catalyst on the rate of a reaction? The catalyst lowers the activation energy and, thus, the amount of energy required by the system.

20. In a chemical equation, how do you show that catalysts are not consumed or chemically altered during a reaction? The catalyst is often written above the yield arrow in the equation.

21. A(n) _____ inhibitor _____ is a substance that interferes with the action of a catalyst.

CHAPTER 18, Reaction Rates and Equilibrium *(continued)*

SECTION 18.2 REVERSIBLE REACTIONS AND EQUILIBRIUM (pages 549–559)

This section shows you how to predict changes in the equilibrium position due to changes in concentration, temperature, and pressure. It teaches you how to write the equilibrium-constant expression for a reaction and calculate its value from experimental data.

▶ Reversible Reactions (pages 549–551)

1. What happens in reversible reactions? In reversible reactions, two opposite reactions occur simultaneously.

2. Is the following sentence true or false? Chemical equilibrium is a state in which the forward and reverse reactions take place at different rates. _____false_____

3. The equilibrium position of a reaction is given by the relative ____concentrations____ of the system's components at equilibrium.

4. Fill in the missing labels on the diagram below with either the words *at equilibrium* or *not at equilibrium*. At equilibrium, how many types of molecules are present in the mixture? ___3___

SO₂ and O₂	2SO₂ + O₂ ⇌ 2SO₃	SO₃
not at equilibrium	at equilibrium	not at equilibrium

5. Use Figure 18.10 on page 550 to answer these questions.

   a. Which graph, left or right, shows an initial concentration of 100% SO_3 and no SO_2? _____right_____

   b. Compare the initial concentrations of the substances shown in the other graph.
   There is twice as much SO_2 as O_2 and no SO_3.

   c. What is the favored substance at equilibrium? How can you tell?
   SO_3, because it has the greatest concentration at equilibrium.

▶ Factors Affecting Equilibrium: Le Châtelier's Principle (pages 552–555)

6. What is Le Châtelier's principle? Le Châtelier's principle states that if a stress is applied to a system in dynamic equilibrium, the system changes to relieve the stress.

Name _____ Date _____ Class _____

7. Circle the letters of the terms that complete the sentence correctly. Stresses that upset the equilibrium of a chemical system include changes in _____ .

   a. concentration   **(c.)** pressure

   b. the amount of catalyst   **(d.)** temperature

8. When you add a product to a reversible chemical reaction, the reaction is always pushed in the direction of _____reactants_____ . When you remove a product, the reaction is pulled in the direction of _____products_____ .

9. Is the following sentence true or false? Increasing the temperature of a chemical reaction causes the equilibrium position of a reaction to shift in the direction that absorbs heat. _____true_____

10. How does increasing pressure affect a chemical system? ___An increase in pressure___ results in a shift in the equilibrium position that favors the formation of a smaller volume of gas.

11. Decreasing the pressure on the system shown in Figure 18.13 on page 554 results in a shift of equilibrium to favor _____the reactants_____ .

▶ Equilibrium Constants (pages 556–559)

12. The equilibrium constant (K_{eq}) is the ratio of ___product___ concentrations to ___reactant___ concentrations at equilibrium, with each concentration raised to a power equal to the number of ___moles___ of that substance in the balanced chemical equation.

13. What are the exponents in the equilibrium-constant expression?
The exponents are the coefficients from the balanced chemical equation.

14. What do the square brackets indicate in the equilibrium-constant expression?
The square brackets indicate the concentrations of substances in moles per liter (mol/L).

15. Is the following sentence true or false? The value of K_{eq} for a reaction depends on the temperature. _____true_____

16. A value of K_{eq} greater than 1 means that ___products___ are favored over ___reactants___ . A value of K_{eq} less than 1 means that ___reactants___ are favored over ___products___ .

CHAPTER 18, Reaction Rates and Equilibrium *(continued)*

SECTION 18.3 SOLUBILITY EQUILIBRIUM (pages 560–565)

This section explains how to calculate the solubility product constant of a slightly soluble salt.

▶ **The Solubility Product Constant** (pages 560–562)

1. What is the solubility product constant (K_{sp})?

   The solubility product constant equals the product of the concentration terms each

   raised to the power of the coefficient of the substance in the dissociation equation.

2. Look at Table 18.1 on page 561. Which ionic compounds are exceptions to the general insolubility of carbonates, phosphates, and sulfites?

   Compounds of the alkali metals and of ammonium ions are exceptions.

3. Look at Table 18.2 on page 562. Which salt is more soluble in water, silver

   bromide (AgBr) or silver chromate (Ag_2CrO_4)? _____silver chromate_____

▶ **The Common Ion Effect** (pages 563–565)

4. A common ion is an ion that is common to both _____salts_____ in a solution.

5. Is the following sentence true or false? The raising of the solubility of a

   substance by the addition of a common ion is called the common ion

   effect. _____false_____

6. A solubility product can be used to predict whether a _____precipitate_____ will form when solutions are mixed.

SECTION 18.4 ENTROPY AND FREE ENERGY (pages 566–573)

This section defines entropy and free energy, and characterizes reactions as spontaneous or nonspontaneous. It also describes how heat change and entropy change determine the spontaneity of a reaction.

▶ **Free Energy and Spontaneous Reactions** (pages 566–568)

1. Free energy is energy that is available to do _____work_____ .

2. Is the following sentence true or false? All processes can be made 100%

   efficient. _____false_____

Name _____ Date _____ Class _____

3. Make a concept map about balanced chemical reactions.

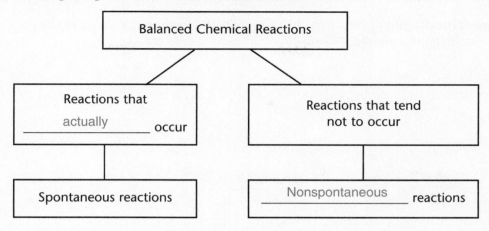

4. Spontaneous reactions are reactions that occur naturally and that favor the

formation of _____products_____ at the specified conditions.

5. Describe four spontaneous reactions mentioned in this section.

a. exploding fireworks _____

b. the decomposition of carbonic acid in water _____

c. the reaction of aqueous solutions of $Cd(NO_3)_2$ and Na_2S to produce solid CdS

d. sugar and oxygen to produce carbon dioxide and water _____

6. What are nonspontaneous reactions?

Nonspontaneous reactions are reactions that do not favor the formation of products

at the specified conditions.

7. Is the following sentence true or false? Some reactions that are non-

spontaneous at one set of conditions may be spontaneous at other

conditions. _____true_____

▶ **Entropy** (pages 568–570)

8. Some factor other than _____heat_____ change must help determine

whether a physical or chemical process is spontaneous.

9. What is entropy? _____Entropy is the measure of the disorder of a system._____

10. The law of disorder states that processes move in the direction of

_____maximum_____ disorder or randomness.

11. Is the following sentence true or false? Entropy decreases when a substance is

divided into parts. _____false_____

CHAPTER 18, Reaction Rates and Equilibrium *(continued)*

12. Number the diagrams below from 1 to 3 to show the increasing entropy of the system. Diagram 1 should show the least amount of entropy.

Liquid	Solid	Gas
2	1	3

13. Does entropy tend to increase or decrease in chemical reactions in which the total number of product molecules is greater than the total number of reactant molecules? _____entropy increases_____

14. Entropy tends to _____increase_____ when temperature increases.

▶ Heat, Entropy, and Free Energy (pages 571–572)

15. What determines whether a reaction is spontaneous?

The size and direction of heat (enthalpy) changes and entropy changes together

determine whether a reaction is spontaneous.

16. Why is an exothermic reaction accompanied by an increase in entropy considered a spontaneous reaction? _____because both factors are favorable_____

17. Is the following sentence true or false? A nonspontaneous reaction, one in which the products are not favored, has heat changes, entropy changes, or both working against it. _____true_____

18. What is the symbol for a change in entropy? _____ΔS_____

▶ Gibbs Free-Energy (pages 572–573)

19. The Gibbs free-energy change (ΔG) is the maximum amount of energy that can be coupled to another process to do useful _____work_____ .

20. What is the equation used to calculate the Gibbs free-energy change?

$\Delta G = \Delta H - T\Delta S$, where ΔH is the change in enthalpy, ΔS is the change in entropy,

and temperature (T) is in kelvins.

21. The numerical value of ΔG is _____negative_____ in spontaneous processes because the system loses free energy; the numerical value of ΔG is _____positive_____ in nonspontaneous processes because the system requires that work be expended to make them go forward at the specified conditions.

 Reading Skill Practice

Writing a summary can help you remember the information you have read. When you write a summary, include only the most important points. Write a summary of the information under the heading *Gibbs Free-Energy,* pages 572–573. Your summary should be shorter than the text on which it is based. Do your work on a separate sheet of paper.

Students' summaries should include the definition of the highlighted term *Gibbs free-energy change,* as well as an explanation of the free-energy equation and the meaning of each term.

SECTION 18.5 THE PROGRESS OF CHEMICAL REACTIONS (pages 575–579)

This section describes how to use experimental rate data to deduce the rate laws for simple chemical reactions. It also shows how to analyze the mechanism for a reaction from an energy diagram.

▶ **Rate Laws (pages 575–577)**

1. What is a one-step reaction? It is a reaction with only one activated complex between the reactants and the products.

2. Is the following sentence true or false? A rate law is an expression relating the rate of a reaction to the concentration of products. _____false_____

3. What is a specific rate constant (k) for a reaction? The constant is a proportionality constant relating the concentrations of reactants to the rate of the reaction.

4. The _____order_____ of a reaction is the power to which the concentration of a reactant must be raised to give the experimentally observed relationship between concentration and rate.

5. In a first-order reaction, the reaction rate is directly proportional to the concentration of _____ .

   a. two or more reactants

   b. both reactants and products

   c. only one reactant

CHAPTER 18, Reaction Rates and Equilibrium *(continued)*

6. How do you determine the actual kinetic order of a reaction?

The actual kinetic order must be determined by experiment.

▶ Reaction Mechanisms (page 578)

7. What is a reaction progress curve? A reaction progress curve is a graph of all the

energy changes that occur as reactants are converted to products.

8. A(n) _____elementary_____ reaction is one in which reactants are converted to products in a single step.

9. Is the following sentence true or false? A reaction mechanism includes some of the elementary reactions of a complex reaction. _____false_____

10. What is an intermediate product of a reaction?

It is a product of one step in the reaction mechanism that becomes a reactant in the

next step in the reaction.

11. Look at Figure 18.28 on page 578. What is one difference between this graph and the chemical equation for this reaction?

The graph shows that the reaction proceeds through five steps; the chemical

equation sums up the five steps into what appears to be one step.

GUIDED PRACTICE PROBLEMS

GUIDED PRACTICE PROBLEM 6 (page 555)

6. How is the equilibrium position of this reaction affected by the following changes?

$$C(s) + H_2O(g) + heat \rightleftharpoons CO(g) + H_2(g)$$

   a. lowering the temperature

   b. increasing the pressure

   c. removing hydrogen

   d. adding water vapor

Analyze

Step 1. Plan a problem-solving strategy.

a-d Use Le Châtelier's principle to analyze the shift in the system effected by each stress.

Solve

Step 2. Apply the problem-solving strategy.

a. Lowering the temperature will shift the equilibrium to the left to produce heat.

b. Increasing the pressure will shift equilibrium to the left because fewer gas molecules are on the reactant side.

c. Removing hydrogen will shift the equilibrium to the right so the system will create more hydrogen gas.

d. Increasing the amount of water vapor will shift the equilibrium position to the right because there is an increase in a reactant.

Evaluate

Step 3. Does the result make sense?

The answers follow Le Châtelier's principle.

CHAPTER 18, Reaction Rates and Equilibrium *(continued)*

GUIDED PRACTICE PROBLEM 7 (page 557)

7. The reaction $N_2(g) + 3H_2(g) \rightleftharpoons 2NH_3(g)$ produces ammonia. At equilibrium, a 1-L flask contains 0.15 mol H_2, 0.25 mol N_2, and 0.10 mol NH_3. Calculate K_{eq} for the reaction.

Analyze

Step 1. List the knowns and the unknown.
Knowns

$[H_2]$ = 0.15 mol/L
_____

$[N_2]$ = 0.25 mol/L
_____

$[NH_3]$ = 0.10 mol/L
_____

K_{eq} (algebraic) = $\dfrac{[NH_3]^2}{[N_2] \times [H_2]^3}$
_____

Unknown

K_{eq} (numerical) = ?
_____

Calculate

Step 2. Solve for the unknowns.
Use the concentrations given and the coefficients from the balanced equation to determine K_{eq}:

$$K_{eq} = \frac{[NH_3]^2}{[N_2] \times [H_2]^3}$$

$$= \frac{0.10^2}{0.25 \times 0.15^3} = 11.85$$

$$= \underline{\quad 12 \quad}$$

GUIDED PRACTICE PROBLEM 9 (page 558)

9. Suppose the following system reaches equilibrium.

$$N_2(g) + O_2(g) \rightleftharpoons 2NO(g)$$

An analysis of the equilibrium mixture in a 1-L flask gives the following results: nitrogen, 0.50 mol; oxygen, 0.50 mol; nitrogen monoxide, 0.020 mol. Calculate K_{eq} for the reaction.

Step 1. List the known values and the unknowns.	Known	Unknown
	$[N_2]$ = 0.50 mol/L	K_{eq} = ?
	$[O_2]$ = 0.50 mol/L	
	$[NO]$ = 0.020 mol/L	

Step 2. Write the K_{eq} for the reaction. It should have three variables.

$$K_{eq} = \frac{[NO]^2}{[N_2] \times [O_2]}$$

Step 3. Substitute the known values in the expression.

$$K_{eq} = \frac{(\boxed{0.020} \text{ mol/L})^2}{\boxed{0.50} \text{ mol/L} \times \boxed{0.50} \text{ mol/L}}$$

Step 4. Solve. Write your answer in scientific notation.

$$K_{eq} = 0.0016 = \boxed{1.6 \times 10^{-3}}$$

CHAPTER 18, Reaction Rates and Equilibrium *(continued)*

GUIDED PRACTICE PROBLEM 18 (page 562)

18. What is the concentration of calcium ions in a saturated calcium carbonate solution at 25°C? ($K_{sp} = 4.5 \times 10^{-9}$)

Analyze

Step 1. List the knowns and the unknown.

Knowns

$K_{sp} = 4.5 \times 10^{-9}$
_____

$K_{sp} = [Ca^{2+}] \times [CO_3^{2-}]$
_____

$CaCO_3 = Ca^{2+} + CO_3^{2-}$
_____

Unknown

$[Ca^{2+}] = ?$
_____

At equilibrium $[Ca^{2+}] = [CO_3^{2-}]$. This fact will be used to solve for the unknown.

Calculate

Step 2. Solve for the unknown.

$K_{sp} = [Ca^{2+}] \times [CO_3^{2-}]$

Make a substitution based on the equilibrium condition stated above:

$K_{sp} = [Ca^{2+}] \times [Ca^{2+}] = [Ca^{2+}]^2 = 4.5 \times 10^{-9}$

Now solve for the unknown:

$[Ca^{2+}] = $ _____ $6.7 \times 10^{-5} \, M$ _____

GUIDED PRACTICE PROBLEM 19 (page 564)

19. What is the concentration of sulfide ion in a 1.0-L solution of iron(II) sulfide to which 0.04 mol of iron(II) nitrate is added? The K_{sp} of FeS is 8×10^{-19}.

Analyze

Step 1. List the knowns and the unknown.
Knowns

$K_{sp} = 8 \times 10^{-19}$

moles of $Fe(NO_3)_2 = 0.04$ mol

volume of solution = 1.0 L

$FeS \rightleftharpoons Fe^{2+} + S^{2-}$

$K_{sp} = [Fe^{2+}] \times [S^{2-}]$

Unknown

$[S^{2-}] = ?\ M$

Let $x = [S^{2-}]$ so that $x + 0.04 = [Fe^{2+}]$

Calculate

Step 2. Solve for the unknown.
Because K_{sp} is very small, simplify by assuming $x << 0.04$, and becomes negligible. Thus $[Fe^{2+}]$ is approximately equal to 0.04 M.

Solve for x in the equation: $K_{sp} = [Fe^{2+}] \times [S^{2-}] = [Fe^{2+}] \times x = 8 \times 10^{-19}$

Rearranging for x gives the result:

$$x = \frac{8 \times 10^{-19}}{[Fe^{2+}]} = \frac{8 \times 10^{-19}}{0.04 \text{ mol}} = 2 \times 10^{-17} M$$

So $[S^{2-}] = \underline{\hspace{1cm} 2 \times 10^{-17} M \hspace{1cm}}$

CHAPTER 18, Reaction Rates and Equilibrium *(continued)*

GUIDED PRACTICE PROBLEM 36 (page 577)

36. Show that the unit of k for a first-order reaction is a reciprocal unit of time, such as a reciprocal second (s^{-1}).

Analyze

Step 1. Plan a problem-solving strategy
The definition of the reaction rate is the change in concentration of a substance per change in time. So using a unit, "concentration" for the numerator and "time" for the denominator, the reaction rate has units [concentration/time].

Use this knowledge algebraically to show the unit for k.

Solve

Step 2. Apply the problem solving strategy.
Because the change in concentration per unit time is proportional to the initial concentration, setting up an equation with units will show this proportionality.

$$\frac{A}{t} = k \times [A]$$

$$\frac{[\text{concentration}]}{[\text{time}]} = k \times [\text{concentration}]$$

Canceling the unit "concentration" from both sides of the equation gives the result:

$$\frac{1}{[\text{time}]} = k$$

The unit of k is $[\text{time}]^{-1}$

Evaluate

Step 3. Does the result make sense?

Units can be treated just as algebraic variables in equations, making

dimensional analysis a useful problem-solving tool.

19 ACIDS, BASES, AND SALTS

SECTION 19.1 ACID–BASE THEORIES (pages 587–593)

This section compares and contrasts acids and bases as defined by the theories of Arrhenius, Brønsted-Lowry, and Lewis. It also identifies conjugate acid–base pairs in acid–base reactions.

▶ Properties of Acids and Bases (pages 587–588)

1. Circle the letters of all the terms that complete the sentence correctly. The properties of acids include _____ .

    a. reacting with metals to produce oxygen

    (b.) giving foods a sour taste

    (c.) forming solutions that conduct electricity

    (d.) causing indicators to change color

2. Bases are compounds that react with acids to form _____water_____ and a(n) _____salt_____ .

3. Circle the letters of all the terms that complete the sentence correctly. The properties of bases include _____ .

    (a.) tasting bitter

    (b.) feeling slippery

    (c.) changing the color of an indicator

    d. always acting as a strong electrolyte

▶ Arrhenius Acids and Bases (pages 588–590)

4. Match the number of ionizable hydrogens with the type of acid.

    ___c___ one   **a.** diprotic

    ___a___ two   **b.** triprotic

    ___b___ three   **c.** monoprotic

5. Is the following sentence true or false? Only the hydrogens in weak polar bonds are ionizable. _____false_____

6. Hydrogen is joined to a very _____electronegative_____ element in a very polar bond.

7. Alkali metals react with water to produce _____basic_____ solutions.

CHAPTER 19, Acids, Bases, and Salts *(continued)*

8. How do concentrated basic solutions differ from other basic solutions?

They are extremely caustic.

▶ Brønsted-Lowry Acids and Bases (pages 590–592)

9. How does the Brønsted-Lowry theory define acids and bases?

The Brønsted-Lowry theory defines an acid as a hydrogen-ion donor and a base

as a hydrogen-ion acceptor.

10. Is the following sentence true or false? Some of the acids and bases included in the Arrhenius theory are not acids and bases according to the Brønsted-Lowry theory. _____false_____

11. Is the following sentence true or false? A conjugate acid is the particle formed when a base gains a hydrogen ion. _____true_____

12. A conjugate _____base_____ is the particle that remains when an acid has donated a hydrogen ion.

13. What is a conjugate acid–base pair? A conjugate acid–base pair consists of two

substances related by the loss or gain of a single hydrogen ion.

14. A substance that can act as both an acid and a base is said to be _____amphoteric_____ .

15. In a reaction with HCl, is water an acid or a base?

Water is a base because it accepts a proton.

▶ Lewis Acids and Bases (pages 592–593)

16. What is a Lewis acid? A Lewis acid is a substance that can accept a pair of

electrons to form a covalent bond.

17. A Lewis base is a substance that can _____donate_____ a pair of electrons to form a covalent bond.

18. Is the following sentence true or false? All the acids and bases included in the Brønsted-Lowry theory are also acids and bases according to the Lewis theory.

_____ true _____

19. Complete this table of acid-base definitions.

Acid–Base Definitions		
Type	**Acid**	**Base**
Brønsted-Lowry	H^+ donor	H^+ acceptor
Lewis	electron-pair acceptor	electron-pair donor
Arrhenius	H^+ producer	OH^- producer

SECTION 19.2 HYDROGEN IONS AND ACIDITY (pages 594–604)

This section classifies solutions as neutral, acidic, or basic, given the hydrogen-ion or hydroxide-ion concentration. It explains how to convert hydrogen-ion concentrations into pH values and hydroxide-ion concentrations into pOH values.

▶ Hydrogen Ions from Water (pages 594-595)

1. What does a water molecule that loses a hydrogen ion become?

It becomes a negatively charged hydroxide ion (OH^-).

2. What does a water molecule that gains a hydrogen ion become?

It becomes a positively charged hydronium ion (H_3O^+).

3. The reaction in which water molecules produce ions is called the

_____ self-ionization _____ of water.

4. In water or aqueous solution, _____ hydrogen ions (H^+) _____ are always joined to

_____ water molecules _____ as hydronium ions (H_3O^+).

5. Is the following sentence true or false? Any aqueous solution in which $[H^+]$ and

$[OH^-]$ are equal is described as a neutral solution. _____ true _____

▶ Ion Product Constant for Water (pages 595–596)

6. What is the ion-product constant for water (K_w)? Give the definition, the

expression, and the value. The ion-product constant for water is the product of the

concentrations of the hydrogen ions and hydroxide ions in water.

$K_w = [H^+] \times [OH^-] = 1.0 \times 10^{-14}$

CHAPTER 19, Acids, Bases, and Salts *(continued)*

7. A(n) _____acidic_____ solution is one in which [H⁺] is greater than [OH⁻].

   A(n) _____basic_____ solution is one in which [H⁺] is less than [OH⁻].

8. Match the type of solution with its hydrogen-ion concentration.

   ___b___ acidic   **a.** less than $1.0 \times 10^{-7} M$

   ___c___ neutral   **b.** greater than $1.0 \times 10^{-7} M$

   ___a___ basic   **c.** $1.0 \times 10^{-7} M$

▶ The pH Concept (pages 596–600)

9. The ___pH___ of a solution is the negative logarithm of the hydrogen-ion concentration.

10. Match the type of solution with its pH.

    ___c___ acidic   **a.** pH > 7.0

    ___b___ neutral   **b.** pH = 7.0

    ___a___ basic   **c.** pH < 7.0

11. Look at Table 19.5 on page 598. What is the approximate [H⁺], the [OH⁻], and the pH of washing soda? _____ 1×10^{-12} mol/L, 1×10^{-2} mol/L, and 12.0 _____

12. The pOH of a solution is the negative logarithm of the _____hydroxide-ion_____ concentration.

13. What is the pOH of a neutral solution? ___7___

14. For pH calculations, in what form should you express the hydrogen-ion concentration? You should express the hydrogen-ion concentration in scientific notation.

15. Look at the pH scale below. Label where you would find acids, bases, and neutral solutions.

pH

| 0 | 1 | 2 | 3 | 4 | 5 | 6 | 7 | 8 | 9 | 10 | 11 | 12 | 13 | 14 |

Acids | Neutral | Bases

10^0 10^{-1} 10^{-2} 10^{-3} 10^{-4} 10^{-5} 10^{-6} 10^{-7} 10^{-8} 10^{-9} 10^{-10} 10^{-11} 10^{-12} 10^{-13} 10^{-14}

16. Is the following sentence true or false? Most pH values are whole numbers.

_____ false _____

17. If [H⁺] is written in scientific notation but its coefficient is not 1, what do you need to calculate pH? You need either a table of common logarithms or a calculator with a log function key.

18. Is the following sentence true or false? You can calculate the hydrogen-ion concentration of a solution if you know the pH. _____ true _____

▶ Measuring pH (pages 600–603)

19. When do you use indicators and when do you use a pH meter to measure pH?

You use indicators for preliminary measurements and for small-volume samples. You use a pH meter for precise and continuous measurements.

20. Why is an indicator a valuable tool for measuring pH?

It is a valuable tool for measuring pH because its acid form and base form have different colors in solution.

21. Why do you need many different indicators to span the entire pH spectrum?

For each indicator, the change from dominating acid form to dominating base form occurs in a narrow range of approximately two pH units.

22. Look at the figure below. Fill in the missing pH color change ranges for the indicators.

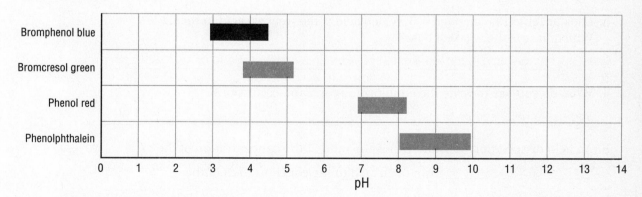

23. List three characteristics that limit the usefulness of indicators.

a. At temperatures other than 25°C, an indicator may change color at a different pH.

b. Indicator color can be distorted if a solution is not colorless.

c. Dissolved salts in a solution can affect the dissociation of the indicator.

CHAPTER 19, Acids, Bases, and Salts (continued)

24. How accurate are measurements of pH obtained with a pH meter?

    to within 0.01 pH unit of the true pH

25. What is the pH of each of the following solutions?

    a. water ___7___

    b. vinegar ___3___

    c. milk of magnesia ___10.5___

26. Is the following sentence true or false? Measurements of pH obtained with a pH meter are typically accurate to within 0.001 pH unit of the true pH.

    _____false_____

SECTION 19.3 STRENGTHS OF ACIDS AND BASES (pages 605–611)

This section defines strong acids and weak acids, and then explains how to calculate an acid dissociation constant. It describes how acids and bases are arranged by strength according to their dissociation constants (K_a) and (K_b).

▶ Strong and Weak Acids and Bases (pages 605–609)

1. What factor is used to classify acids as strong or weak?

   Acids are classified by the degree to which they ionize in water.

2. Strong acids are _____completely_____ ionized in aqueous solution; weak acids ionize _____only slightly_____ in aqueous solution.

3. Look at Table 19.6 on page 605. Which acid is the weakest acid in the table? Which base is the weakest base?

   Hypochlorous acid is the weakest acid. Ammonia is the weakest base.

4. What do you use to write the equilibrium-constant expression?

   You use a balanced chemical equation.

5. An acid dissociation constant (K_a) is the ratio of the concentration of the _____dissociated_____ form of an acid to the concentration of the _____undissociated_____ form.

6. What is another name for dissociation constants?

   Another name is ionization constants.

7. Is the following sentence true or false? The stronger an acid is, the smaller its K_a value. _____false_____

8. A diprotic acid has _____two_____ dissociation constants.

Name _____ Date _____ Class _____

9. Look at Table 19.7 on page 607. What is the second dissociation constant for the triprotic phosphoric acid? _____ $K_a = 6.2 \times 10^{-8}$ _____

10. Weak bases react with water to form the hydroxide ion and the _____ conjugate acid _____ of the base.

11. A base dissociation constant (K_b) is the ratio of the concentration of the _____ conjugate acid _____ times the concentration of the hydroxide ion to the concentration of the _____ conjugate base _____ .

12. What does the magnitude of the base dissociation constant (K_b) indicate?

It indicates the ability of a weak base to compete with the very strong base OH^- for

hydrogen ions.

13. The words *concentrated* and *dilute* indicate how much acid or base is _____ dissolved _____ in solution.

14. Is the following sentence true or false? The words strong or weak refer to the extent of ionization or dissociation of an acid or base. _____ true _____

▶ **Calculating Dissociation Constants** (pages 609–610)

15. Is the following sentence true or false? You can calculate the acid dissociation constant (K_a) of a weak acid from experimental data. _____ true _____

16. To measure the equilibrium concentrations of all substances present at equilibrium for a weak acid, what two conditions must you know?

You must know the initial molar concentration of the acid and the pH (or $[H_3O^+]$) of

the solution at equilibrium.

Reading Skill Practice

By looking carefully at photographs and drawings in textbooks, you can better understand what you have read. Look carefully at Figure 19.16 on page 606. What important idea does this drawing communicate? Do your work on a separate sheet of paper.

The illustration compares the extent of dissociation of strong, weak, and very weak acids.

CHAPTER 19, Acids, Bases, and Salts *(continued)*

SECTION 19.4 NEUTRALIZATION REACTIONS (pages 612–616)

This section explains how acid–base titration is used to calculate the concentration of an acid or a base. It also explains the concept of equivalence in neutralization reactions.

▶ Acid–Base Reactions (pages 612–613)

1. Is the following sentence true or false? Acids react with compounds containing hydroxide ions to form water and a salt. _____true_____

2. What does the reaction of an acid with a base produce?
   It produces water and a salt. _____

3. In general, reactions in which an acid and a base react in an aqueous solution to produce a salt and water are called _____neutralization_____ reactions.

4. Look at Table 19.9 on page 613. Circle the letter of the salt that is used for photographic emulsions.

   a. calcium chloride   **c.** silver bromide

   b. potassium chloride   **d.** sodium chloride

5. Salts are compounds consisting of a(n) _____anion_____ from an acid and a(n) _____cation_____ from a base.

▶ Titration (pages 613–616)

6. How can you determine the concentration of an acid or base in a solution?
   You can perform a neutralization reaction. _____

7. Complete the flow chart below showing the steps of a neutralization reaction.

A measured volume of an acid solution of _____unknown_____ concentration is added to a flask.

   ↓

Several drops of the _____indicator_____ are added to the solution while the flask is gently swirled.

   ↓

Measured volumes of a base of _____known_____ concentration are mixed into the acid until the indicator changes _____color_____ .

8. The process of adding a known amount of solution of known concentration to determine the concentration of another solution is called _____ titration _____ .

9. What is the solution of known concentration called?

It is called the standard solution.

SECTION 19.5 SALTS IN SOLUTION (pages 618–622)

This section demonstrates with equations how buffers resist changes in pH. It also explains how to calculate the solubility product constant of a slightly soluble salt.

▶ Salt Hydrolysis (pages 618–620)

1. What is salt hydrolysis? Salt hydrolysis occurs when the cations or anions of a dissociated salt remove hydrogen ions from or donate hydrogen ions to water.

2. Complete this table of the rules for hydrolysis of a salt.

Reactants		Products
_____Strong_____ acid + _____Strong_____ base		Neutral solution
Strong acid + Weak base		_____Acidic_____ solution
_____Weak_____ acid + _____Strong_____ base		Basic solution

▶ Buffers (pages 620–622)

3. What are buffers? Buffers are solutions in which the pH remains relatively constant when small amounts of acid or base are added.

4. A buffer is a solution of a _____ weak _____ acid and one of its salts, or a solution of a _____ weak _____ base and one of its salts.

5. Is the following sentence true or false? The buffer capacity is the amount of acid or base that can be added to a buffer solution before a significant change in pH occurs. _____ true _____

CHAPTER 19, Acids, Bases, and Salts (continued)

GUIDED PRACTICE PROBLEMS

EXTRA PRACTICE PROBLEM (similar to Practice Problem 13, page 600)

13. Find the value of $[OH^-]$ for a solution with a pH of 8.00.

If pH = 8.00, pOH = 6.00 because pH + pOH = 14.

$pOH = -\log [OH^-]$

$6.00 = -\log [OH^-]$

$-6.00 = \log [OH^-]$

$10^{-6.00} = 10^{\log [OH^-]}$

$[OH^-] = 10^{-6}$

GUIDED PRACTICE PROBLEM 16b (page 601)

16b. Calculate the pH of this solution: $[H^+] = 8.3 \times 10^{-10} M$.

Step 1. Identify the known and unknown values.

Known

$[H^+] = \boxed{8.3} \times 10^{-10} M$

Unknown

pH = ?

Step 2. Substitute values into the pH equation.

$pH = -\log [H^+]$
$= -\log (8.3 \times \boxed{10^{-10}})$

Step 3. The logarithm of a product equals the sum of the logs of its factors.

$= - (\log \boxed{8.3} + \log \boxed{10^{-10}})$

Step 4. Evaluate log 8.3 by using a calculator. Evaluate $\log 10^{-10}$ by using the definition of logarithm.

$= -(0.919 + \boxed{-10})$

Step 5. Add and simplify. Write your answer with two significant figures to the right of the decimal point.

$= -(-9.081) = \boxed{9.08}$

GUIDED PRACTICE PROBLEM 22 (page 610)

22. For a solution of methanoic acid exactly 0.1 M, $[H^+] = 4.2 \times 10^{-3}M$. Calculate the K_a of methanoic acid.

Analyze

Step 1. What is known about the acid?

It is a 0.1M solution, $[H^+] = 4.2 \times 10^{-3}M$, and the equation for dissociation is

$HCOOH \rightleftharpoons HCOO^- + H^+$.

Step 2. What is the unknown? $\underline{K_a}$

Step 3. What is the expression for the K_a of methanoic acid?

$$K_a = \frac{[HCOO^-] \times [H^+]}{[HCOOH]}$$

Solve

Step 4. What expression can you write to find the equilibrium concentration of HCOOH?

$0.1000 - 4.2 \times 10^{-3} = 0.0958$

Step 5. Substitute values into the formula for K_a and solve.

$$K_a = \frac{(4.2 \times 10^{-3}) \times (4.2 \times 10^{-3})}{0.0958} = \frac{1.764 \times 10^{-5}}{0.0958}$$

$$= 184.1 \times 10^{-6} = 1.8 \times 10^{-4}$$

Analyze

Step 6. Look at Table 19.7 on page 607. Explain why your answer is reasonable.

The value for K_a is the same as the one given in the table.

Name _____ Date _____ Class _____

20 OXIDATION–REDUCTION REACTIONS

SECTION 20.1 THE MEANING OF OXIDATION AND REDUCTION (pages 631–638)

This section explains oxidation and reduction in terms of the loss or gain of electrons, and describes the characteristics of a redox reaction. It also explains how to identify oxidizing and reducing agents.

▶ What are Oxidation and Reduction? (pages 631–635)

1. What was the original meaning of the term *oxidation*? <u>Oxidation originally meant</u> <u>the combination of an element with oxygen to produce an oxide.</u>

2. Circle the letter of each sentence that is true about oxidation.

   (a.) Gasoline, wood, coal, and natural gas (methane) can all burn in air, producing oxides of carbon.

   b. All oxidation processes involve burning.

   (c.) Bleaching is an example of oxidation.

   (d.) Rusting is an example of oxidation.

3. Look at Figure 20.2 and Figure 20.3 on page 632. Describe what is happening in each chemical reaction.

   a. $C(s) + O_2(g) \longrightarrow CO_2(g)$ <u>Carbon and oxygen are combining to produce</u> <u>carbon dioxide and heat.</u>

   b. $4Fe(s) + 3O_2(g) \longrightarrow 2Fe_2O_3(s)$ <u>Iron atoms slowly combine with oxygen in moist</u> <u>air to produce compounds such as iron(III) oxide.</u>

4. What is the name of the process that is the opposite of oxidation? <u>reduction</u>

5. Circle the letter of each sentence that is true about oxidation and reduction.

   (a.) Oxidation never occurs without reduction and reduction never occurs without oxidation.

   (b.) You need to add heat in order to reduce iron ore to produce metallic iron.

   c. When iron oxide is reduced to metallic iron, it gains oxygen.

   (d.) Oxidation–reduction reactions are also known as redox reactions.

CHAPTER 20, Oxidation–Reduction Reactions *(continued)*

6. What substance is heated along with iron ore in order to reduce the metal oxide to metallic iron? _charcoal (carbon)_

7. Look at the chemical equation for the reduction of iron ore on page 632. When iron ore is reduced to metallic iron, what oxidation reaction occurs at the same time? _Carbon combines with oxygen from the iron(III) oxide to form carbon dioxide._

8. Is the following sentence true or false? The concepts of oxidation and reduction have been extended to include many reactions that do not even involve oxygen. _true_

9. What is understood about electrons in redox reactions?

Redox reactions involve a shift of electrons between reactants.

10. In the table below, fill in either "Gain" or "Loss" to correctly describe what happens to electrons or oxygen during oxidation or reduction.

	Oxidation	**Reduction**
Electrons	Loss	Gain
Oxygen	Gain	Loss

11. Look at Figure 20.4 on page 633. Circle the letter of each sentence that is true about the reaction of magnesium and sulfur.

   a. When magnesium and sulfur are heated together, they undergo a redox reaction to form magnesium sulfide.

   b. Electrons are transferred from the metal atoms to the nonmetal atoms in this reaction.

   c. When magnesium atoms lose electrons and sulfur atoms gain electrons, the atoms become less stable.

   d. Magnesium is the oxidizing agent and sulfur is the reducing agent in this reaction.

12. Is the following sentence true or false? In any redox reaction, complete electron transfer must occur. _false_

13. Is the following sentence true or false? A redox reaction may produce covalent compounds. _true_

Name _____ Date _____ Class _____

14. Draw arrows showing the shift of bonding electrons during formation of a water molecule. Then complete the table listing the characteristics of this reaction.

Formation of Water by Reaction of Hydrogen and Oxygen	
Chemical equation	$2H_2(g) + O_2(g) \longrightarrow 2H_2O(l)$
Shift of bonding electrons	away from hydrogen and toward oxygen
Reduced element	oxygen
Oxidized element	hydrogen
Reducing agent	hydrogen
Oxidizing agent	oxygen
Is heat released or absorbed?	Heat is released.

15. For each process described below, label it *O* if it is an oxidation or *R* if it is a reduction.

_____O_____ **a.** Addition of oxygen to carbon or carbon compounds

_____R_____ **b.** Removal of a metal from its ore

_____R_____ **c.** Complete gain of electrons in an ionic reaction

_____O_____ **d.** Shift of electrons away from an atom in a covalent bond

_____R_____ **e.** Gain of hydrogen by a covalent compound

▶ **Corrosion** (pages 636–638)

16. Circle the letter of each sentence that is true about corrosion.

   a. Preventing and repairing damage from corrosion of metals requires billions of dollars every year.

   b. Iron corrodes by being oxidized to ions of iron by oxygen.

   c. Water in the environment slows down the rate of corrosion.

   d. The presence of salts and acids increases the rate of corrosion by producing conducting solutions that make the transfer of electrons easier.

CHAPTER 20, Oxidation–Reduction Reactions *(continued)*

17. Why are gold and platinum called noble metals? because gold and platinum are
very resistant to losing their electrons through corrosion

18. Look at Figure 20.6 on page 636. Why is corrosion desirable in the situation
shown? In this case, corrosion forms a patina that enhances the appearance of the
buildings.

19. Look at Figure 20.7 on page 636. Complete the sketch below to show how
oxides form on the surface of each metal. Explain how differences between the
oxides affect further corrosion of the metals.

Aluminum oxide forms a tightly packed protective layer that does not admit water.

Because iron(III) oxide is not tightly packed, it allows water to penetrate and attack

the metal below.

SECTION 20.2 OXIDATION NUMBERS (pages 639–643)

*This section explains how to determine the oxidation number of an atom of
any element in a pure substance and defines oxidation and reduction in terms
of a change in oxidation number.*

▶ Assigning Oxidation Numbers (pages 639–641)

1. Is the following sentence true or false? As a general rule, a bonded atom's
oxidation number is the charge that it would have if the electrons in the bond
were assigned to the more electronegative element. _____true_____

2. For each binary ionic compound listed in the table, write the symbols for both
ions, their ionic charges, and their oxidation numbers.

Compound	Ions	Ionic Charges	Oxidation Numbers
NaCl	Na$^+$	1+	+1
	Cl$^-$	1−	−1
CaF$_2$	Ca^{2+}	2+	+2
	F$^-$	1−	−1

3. Is the following sentence true or false? Even though water is a molecular compound, you can still obtain oxidation numbers for the bonded elements by imagining that the electrons contributed by the hydrogen atoms are completely transferred to oxygen. _____true_____

4. Write the oxidation number, or the sum of the oxidation numbers, for the given atoms, ions, or compounds.

__+2__ **a.** Cu(II) ion

__+1__ **b.** Hydrogen in water

__−1__ **c.** Hydrogen in sodium hydride (NaH)

__0__ **d.** Potassium sulfate (K_2SO_4)

▶ Oxidation-Number Changes in Chemical Reactions (page 642)

5. Label each change *O* if it describes oxidation or *R* if it describes reduction.

__R__ **a.** Decrease in the oxidation number of an element

__O__ **b.** Increase in the oxidation number of an element

SECTION 20.3 BALANCING REDOX EQUATIONS (pages 645–654)

This section explains how to use the oxidation-number-change and half-reaction methods to balance redox equations.

▶ Identifying Redox Reactions (pages 645–647)

1. Name two kinds of reactions that are not redox reactions.

Double-replacement reactions and acid–base reactions are not redox reactions.

2. Look at Figure 20.15b on page 645. Write the oxidation numbers of all the elements in the reactants and products. Then answer the questions about the reaction.

	Reactants		**Products**	
	Zinc	Hydrochloric acid	Zinc chloride	Hydrogen
Oxidation numbers	0	+1 −1	+2 −1	0
Chemical equation	Zn(*s*) +	HCl(*aq*) ⟶	ZnCl$_2$(*aq*) +	H$_2$(*g*)

a. Is this a redox reaction? _____yes_____

b. Which element is oxidized? How do you know?

Zinc; the oxidation number for zinc increases from 0 to +2.

c. Which element is reduced? How do you know?

Hydrogen; the oxidation number for hydrogen decreases from +1 to 0.

CHAPTER 20, Oxidation–Reduction Reactions *(continued)*

3. When a solution changes color during a reaction, what can you conclude about the reaction that has taken place?

   The reaction could be a redox reaction.

▶ Two Ways to Balance Redox Equations (pages 647–652)

4. Answer these questions to help you balance the following equation using the oxidation-number-change method.

   $$H_2(g) + O_2(g) \longrightarrow H_2O(l) \text{ (unbalanced)}$$

   a. What are the oxidation numbers for each atom in the equation?

   $$\overset{0}{H_2}(g) + \overset{0}{O_2}(g) \longrightarrow \overset{+1\ -2}{H_2O}$$

   b. Which element is oxidized in this reaction? Which is reduced?

   Hydrogen is oxidized; oxygen is reduced.

   c. Use your answers to question *a* above to balance the equation. Write the coefficients needed to make the total change in oxidation number equal to 0.

   $$\overset{0}{H_2}(g) + \overset{0}{O_2}(g) \longrightarrow \overset{+1\ -2}{H_2O}(l)$$

   $$\boxed{2} \times +1 \qquad \boxed{1} \times -2$$

   d. What is the final balanced equation? $2H_2(g) + O_2(g) \longrightarrow 2H_2O(l)$

5. The equations for which reactions are balanced separately when using the half-reaction method? The oxidation and reduction equations are balanced separately.

6. For what kind of reaction is the half-reaction method particularly useful?
   ionic reactions in solution

▶ **Choosing a Balancing Method** (page 653)

7. Why would you choose to use oxidation-number changes to balance an equation?

Because the species oxidized and reduced only appear once on each side of the

equation and no acids or bases are involved.

8. What method would you choose to balance an equation for a reaction that takes place in an acidic or alkaline solution?

the half-reaction method

 # Reading Skill Practice

A flowchart can help you to remember the order in which events occur. On a separate sheet of paper, create a flowchart that describes the steps for the oxidation-number-change method. This process is explained on page 648 of your textbook.

Students' flowcharts should include a box for each of the five steps shown on pages 663–664.

CHAPTER 20, Oxidation–Reduction Reactions *(continued)*

GUIDED PRACTICE PROBLEM

GUIDED PRACTICE PROBLEM 9 (page 641)

9. Determine the oxidation number of each element in these substances.

a. S_2O_3

Step 1. What is the oxidation number for oxygen? Use rule 3. ____−2____

Step 2. What is the oxidation number for all of the oxygen atoms?

$-2 \times 3 = -6$

Step 3. What is the oxidation number for all of the sulfur atoms? ____+6____

Step 4. What is the oxidation number for each sulfur atom? ____+3____

Step 5. How do you know your answers are correct?

The total of the oxidation numbers for all atoms must equal zero.

b. Na_2O_2

Step 1. What is the oxidation number of oxygen? Use rule 3.

(Hint: This compound is a peroxide.) ____−1____

Step 2. What is the oxidation number of sodium? ____+1____

Step 3. How do you know your answer is correct?

The oxidation number for both oxygen atoms is ____−2____ . The sum of the

oxidation numbers for all the atoms must be ____zero____ . Therefore, the oxidation

number for both sodium atoms must equal ____+2____ .

c. P_2O_5

Step 1. What is the oxidation number for oxygen? Use rule 3. ____−2____

Step 2. What is the oxidation number for all of the oxygen atoms?

$-2 \times 5 =$ ____−10____

Step 3. What is the oxidation number for all of the phosphorous atoms? ____+10____

Step 4. What is the oxidation number for each phosphorous atom?

$+10 \div 2 =$ ____+5____

Step 5. How do you know your answers are correct?

The total of the oxidation numbers for all of the atoms must be zero.

d. NH_4^+

Step 1. What is the oxidation number for hydrogen? Use rule 2. ____+1____

Step 2. What is the oxidation number for all of the oxygen atoms?

$+1 \times 4 =$ ____+4____

Step 3. What is the oxidation number for the nitrogen atom? ____−3____

Step 4. How do you know your answers are correct?

The total of the oxidation numbers for all of the atoms must equal the net charge

of the ion.

e. $Ca(OH)_2$

Step 1. What is the oxidation number for oxygen? Use rule 3. ____−2____

Step 2. What is the oxidation number for all of the oxygen atoms?

$-2 \times 2 =$ ____−4____

Step 3. What is the oxidation number for hydrogen? Use rule 2. ____+1____

What is the oxidation number for the hydroxide (OH)?

$-2 + +1 =$ ____−1____

Step 5. What is the oxidation number for all of the hydroxide?

$-1 \times 2 =$ ____−2____

Step 6. What is the oxidation number for the calcium atom? ____+2____

Step 7. How do you know your answers are correct?

The total of all of the oxidation numbers for all of the atoms must be zero.

f. $Al_2(SO_4)_3$

Step 1. What is the charge of the polyatomic
sulfate ion? ____−2____

Step 2. What is the oxidation number of
oxygen? Use rule 3. ____−2____

Step 3. What is the oxidation number
of all of the oxygen atoms? ____$-2 \times 4 = +8$____

Step 4. What is the oxidation number
of the sulfur atom? ____$+6 \ (8 - 2)$____

Step 5. What is the oxidation number
of the aluminum ion? ____+3____

CHAPTER 20, Oxidation–Reduction Reactions *(continued)*

EXTRA PRACTICE (similar to Practice Problem 19, page 649)

19. Balance this redox equation using the oxidation-number-change method.

To make the oxidation numbers balance, you must multiply the oxidation

number of sodium by _____two_____ . Add a coefficient of ___2___ in front of

elemental sodium, but not in front of sodium sulfate because the sodium in

sodium sulfate has a subscript of ___2___ . The balanced equation is

_____$2Na(s) + S(s) \longrightarrow Na_2S(s)$_____ .

ELECTROCHEMISTRY

21

SECTION 21.1 ELECTROCHEMICAL CELLS (pages 663–670)

This section describes how redox reactions interconvert electrical energy and chemical energy. It also explains the structure of a dry cell and identifies the substances that are oxidized and reduced.

▶ **Electrochemical Processes** (pages 663–665)

1. What do the silver plating of tableware and the manufacture of aluminum have in common?

Both processes use electricity.

Look at Figure 21.1 on page 663 and the related text to help you answer Questions 2–6.

2. In what form are the reactants when the reaction starts?

A solid strip of zinc is placed in an aqueous solution of copper sulfate.

3. What kind of reaction occurs? Is it spontaneous?

a redox reaction; yes

4. Which substance is oxidized in the reaction? _____ zinc _____

5. Which substance is reduced? _____ copper ions _____

6. Which atoms lose electrons and which ions gain electrons during the reaction?

Zinc atoms lose electrons as copper ions gain electrons.

7. Look at Table 21.1 on page 664. What information in this table explains why the reaction in Figure 21.1 occurs spontaneously?

Zinc is higher in the table than copper. This means that zinc is more active and more

easily oxidized than copper. Thus, the reaction between zinc atoms and copper ions

is spontaneous.

8. What happens when a copper strip is placed in a solution of zinc sulfate? Explain.

Nothing happens. Copper metal is not oxidized by zinc ions.

9. The flow of _____ electrons _____ from zinc to copper is an electric

_____ current _____ .

CHAPTER 21, Electrochemistry *(continued)*

10. Circle the letter of each sentence that is true about electrochemical cells.

    (a.) An electrochemical cell either produces an electric current or uses an electric current to produce a chemical change.

    (b.) Redox reactions occur in electrochemical cells.

    (c.) For an electrochemical cell to be a source of useful electrical energy, the electrons must pass through an external circuit.

    d. An electrochemical cell can convert chemical energy to electrical energy, but not electrical energy into chemical energy.

▶ Voltaic Cells (pages 665–667)

For Questions 11–15, match each description with the correct term by writing its letter in the blank.

_____c_____ 11. Any electrochemical cell used to convert chemical energy into electrical energy

_____d_____ 12. One part of a voltaic cell in which either reduction or oxidation occurs

_____e_____ 13. The electrode at which oxidation occurs

_____b_____ 14. A tube containing a strong electrolyte, which allows transport of ions between the half-cells

_____a_____ 15. The electrode at which reduction occurs

a. cathode

b. salt bridge

c. voltaic cell

d. half-cell

e. anode

▶ Using Voltaic Cells as Energy Sources (pages 667–670)

16. Look at Figure 21.4 on page 667. How is a common dry cell constructed?

    A common dry cell consists of a zinc container filled with an electrolyte paste of manganese(IV) oxide, zinc chloride, ammonium chloride, and water. The paste surrounds a central graphite rod.

17. Why are alkaline cells better and longer lasting than common cells?

    The design eliminates the build up of ammonia gas and maintains the zinc electrode, which corrodes more slowly under alkaline conditions.

18. Which element is oxidized in a dry cell? Which element is reduced?

    zinc; maganese

Name _____ Date _____ Class _____

19. What is a battery? _A battery is a group of cells connected together._

20. How many voltaic cells are connected inside a lead storage battery typically found in a car? About how many volts are produced by each cell and what is the total voltage of such a battery?

A 12-V car battery consists of six voltaic cells. Each cell produces about 2 volts

making the total voltage 12 volts.

21. Look at Figure 21.5 on page 668. In the diagram below label the following parts of a lead storage battery: electrolyte, anode, and cathode. Also indicate where oxidation and reduction occur while the battery is discharging.

electrolyte

anode, oxidation

cathode, reduction

22. Are the following sentences true or false? As a lead storage battery discharges, lead sulfate builds up on the electrodes. Recharging the battery reverses this process. _____true_____

23. Name two advantages of fuel cells. _They do not need to be recharged and they can_

be designed to emit no pollutants.

 # Reading Skill Practice

Outlining is a way to help you understand and remember what you have read. Write an outline for Section 21.1 *Electrochemical Cells*. Begin your outline by copying the headings in the textbook. Under each heading, write the main idea. Then list details that support, or back up, the main idea. Do your work on a separate sheet of paper.

Students should use the five subheads in the textbook. The section's main ideas should form the next level of the outline.

CHAPTER 21, Electrochemistry *(continued)*

SECTION 21.2 HALF-CELLS AND CELL POTENTIALS (pages 671–677)

This section defines standard cell potential and standard reduction potential. It also explains how to use standard reduction potential to calculate standard cell potential.

▶ **Electrical Potential (page 671)**

1. What unit is usually used to measure electrical potential?

   Electric potential is usually measured in volts.

2. What is the equation for cell potential? _____ $E^0_{cell} = E^0_{red} - E^0_{oxid}$ _____

▶ **Standard Cell Potential (page 672)**

3. What value have chemists assigned as the standard reduction potential of the hydrogen electrode? _____ 0.00 V _____

4. Describe a standard hydrogen electrode. A standard hydrogen electrode consists of a platinum electrode coated with platinum black, immersed in a 1.0*M* hydrogen-ion solution with hydrogen gas bubbled into the solution.

▶ **Standard Reduction Potentials (pages 672–675)**

5. Use of a standard hydrogen electrode allows scientists to determine the _____ standard reduction potential _____ for many half-cells.

6. Look at Figure 21.10 on page 673. Which substance, zinc metal or hydrogen gas, has a greater potential to be oxidized? How can you tell?

   Zinc metal has a greater potential to be oxidized. E^0_{cell} is positive, showing that current is flowing away from zinc as it is oxidized.

7. In the diagram below use the value given for E^0_{cell} above the voltmeter and Table 21.2 to identify the chemical substances in the left half-cell. Use symbols to label the metal electrode and the ions in the half-cell. Also label the cathode and the anode.

Name _____ Date _____ Class _____

▶ **Calculating Standard Cell Potentials** (pages 675–677)

8. If the cell potential for a given redox reaction is _____positive_____,
then the reaction is _____spontaneous_____ . If the cell potential is
_____negative_____ , then the reaction is _____nonspontaneous_____ .

SECTION 21.3 ELECTROLYTIC CELLS (pages 678–683)

This section differentiates electrolytic cells from voltaic cells, and lists uses of electrolytic cells. It also identifies the products of the electrolysis of brine, molten sodium chloride, and water.

▶ Electrolytic vs. Voltaic Cells (pages 678–679)

1. An electrochemical cell used to cause a chemical change through the
application of electrical energy is called _____an electrolytic cell_____ .

2. For each sentence below, fill in *V* if it is true about voltaic cells, *E* if it is true about electrolytic cells, and *B* if it is true about both voltaic and electrolytic cells.

___E___ **a.** Electrons are pushed by an outside power source.

___B___ **b.** Reduction occurs at the cathode and oxidation occurs at the anode.

___V___ **c.** The flow of electrons is the result of a spontaneous redox reaction.

___B___ **d.** Electrons flow from the anode to the cathode.

▶ Electrolysis of Water (page 680)

3. Write the net reaction for the electrolysis of water.

$2H_2O(l) \longrightarrow 2H_2(g) + O_2(g)$

▶ Electrolysis of Brine (page 681)

4. Which three important industrial chemicals are produced through the electrolysis of brine?

chlorine gas, hydrogen gas, and sodium hydroxide

5. Why are the sodium ions not reduced to sodium metal during the electrolysis of brine?

Water molecules are more easily reduced than sodium ions.

▶ Other Applications of Electrolytic Cells (page 682)

6. Deposition of a thin layer of metal on an object in an electrolytic cell is called
_____electroplating_____ .

7. The object to be plated is made the _____cathode_____ in the cell.

CHAPTER 21, Electrochemistry *(continued)*

GUIDED PRACTICE PROBLEM

GUIDED PRACTICE PROBLEM 8 (page 676)

8. A voltaic cell is constructed using the following half-reactions.

$Cu^{2+}(aq) + 2e^- \longrightarrow Cu(s)$ $\qquad$ $E^0_{Cu^{2+}} = +0.34\,V$

$Al^{3+}(aq) + 3e^- \longrightarrow Al(s)$ $\qquad$ $E^0_{Al^{3+}} = -1.66\,V$

Determine the cell reaction and calculate the standard cell potential.

Analyze

Step 1. What are the known values?

$E^0_{Cu^{2+}} = +0.34\,V$ and $E^0_{Al^{3+}} = -1.66\,V$

Step 2. Which half-reaction is a reduction? An oxidation?

Reduction: $\underline{\qquad Cu^{2+}(aq) + 2e^- \longrightarrow Cu(s) \qquad}$

Oxidation: $\underline{\qquad Al^{3+}(aq) + 3e^- \longrightarrow Al(s) \qquad}$

Step 3. Write both half-reactions in the direction they actually occur.

$Cu^{2+}(aq) + 2e^- \longrightarrow Cu(s)$ $\qquad$ $Al(s) \longrightarrow Al^{3+}(aq) + 3e^-$

Step 4. What is the expression for the standard cell potential?

$E^0_{cell} = \underline{\qquad E^0_{red} - E^0_{oxid} \qquad}$

Calculate

Step 5. Write the cell reaction by adding the half-reactions, making certain that the number of electrons lost equals the number of electrons gained. The electrons gained and lost will cancel out.

$\boxed{3}\;[Cu^{2+}(aq) + 2e^- \longrightarrow Cu(s)]$

$\boxed{2}\;[Al(s) \longrightarrow Al^{3+}(aq) + 3e^-]$

$\boxed{2Al(s) + 3Cu^{2+}(aq) \longrightarrow 2Al^{3+}(aq) + 3Cu(s)}$

Step 6. Calculate the standard cell potential.

$E^0_{cell} = \underline{\quad +0.34\,V - (-1.66\,V) = +2.00\,V \quad}$

Evaluate

Step 7. How do you know that the cell reaction is correct?

The number of atoms and ions is the same on both sides of the reaction.

Step 8. When a reaction is spontaneous, will the standard cell potential be positive or negative?

In a spontaneous reaction, the standard cell potential must be positive.

22 HYDROCARBON COMPOUNDS

SECTION 22.1 HYDROCARBONS (pages 693–701)

This section describes the bonding in hydrocarbons and distinguishes straight-chain from branched-chain alkanes. It also provides rules for naming branch-chained alkanes.

▶ Organic Chemistry and Hydrocarbons (pages 693–694)

1. What is organic chemistry? It is the study of the chemistry of carbon compounds.

2. Organic compounds that contain only carbon and hydrogen are called ____hydrocarbons____ .

3. Is the following sentence true or false? Hydrogen atoms are the only atoms that can bond to the carbon atoms in a hydrocarbon. ____false____

4. Circle the letter of each statement that is true about carbon's ability to form bonds.

   (a.) Carbon atoms have four valence electrons.

   b. Carbon atoms always form three covalent bonds.

   (c.) Carbon atoms can form stable bonds with other carbon atoms.

▶ Alkanes (pages 694–699)

5. Is the following sentence true or false? Alkanes contain only single covalent bonds. ____true____

6. What is the simplest alkane? ____methane____

7. What are straight-chain alkanes? They contain any number of carbon atoms, one after another, in a chain.

8. The names of all alkanes end with the suffix ____-ane____ .

Match the name of the straight-chain alkane with the number of carbon atoms it contains.

_d_	**9.** nonane	**a.** 3
_a_	**10.** propane	**b.** 4
_c_	**11.** heptane	**c.** 7
_b_	**12.** butane	**d.** 9

13. The straight-chain alkanes form a(n) ____homologous series____ because there is an incremental change of a CH_2 group from one compound in the series to the next.

CHAPTER 22, Hydrocarbon Compounds *(continued)*

14. Circle the letter of each condensed structural formula for pentane.

    a. C_5H_{12}

    (**b.**) $CH_3CH_2CH_2CH_2CH_3$

    (**c.**) $CH_3(CH_2)_3CH_3$

    (**d.**) C — C — C — C — C

15. The IUPAC system uses _____*prefixes*_____ to show the number of carbon atoms in a straight-chain alkane.

16. A(n) _____*substituent*_____ is an atom or group of atoms that replaces a hydrogen in a hydrocarbon molecule.

17. Alkyl groups are named by removing the *-ane* ending of the parent

hydrocarbon and adding _____*-yl*_____ .

18. What is a branched-chain alkane? __*It is an alkane with one or more alkyl groups.*__

19. Circle the letter of the correct IUPAC name for the molecule below.

$$CH_3-\underset{\underset{CH_3}{|}}{\overset{\overset{CH_3}{|}}{C}}-CH_2-\underset{}{\overset{\overset{CH_3}{|}}{CH}}-CH_3$$

    a. 2,2,4-triethylpentane

    b. 3-methylpentane

    (**c.**) 2,2,4-trimethylpentane

20. Draw a condensed structural formula for 2-methylhexane.

$$CH_3-\underset{\underset{CH_3}{|}}{CH}-CH_2-CH_2-CH_2-CH_3 \text{ or } C-\underset{\underset{C}{|}}{C}-C-C-C-C$$

▶ Properties of Alkanes (page 700)

21. Why are hydrocarbon molecules such as alkanes nonpolar? *Hydrocarbon molecules such as alkanes are nonpolar because the electron pair in a carbon–hydrogen or a carbon–carbon bond is shared almost equally by the nuclei of the atoms involved.*

22. Hydrocarbons and other nonpolar molecules are not attracted to *water or polar molecules* .

Reading Skill Practice

A flowchart can help you to remember the order in which events occur. On a separate sheet of paper, create a flowchart that describes the steps for naming branched-chain alkanes using the IUPAC system. This process is explained on page 698.

Students' flowcharts will vary. A typical flowchart should include a box for each of the numbered steps on page 698.

SECTION 22.2 UNSATURATED HYDROCARBONS (pages 702–703)

This section explains the difference between unsaturated and saturated hydrocarbons. It also describes the difference between alkenes and alkynes.

▶ **Alkenes (page 702)**

1. What is an alkene?

   It is a hydrocarbon containing one or more carbon–carbon double covalent bonds.

2. Organic compounds that contain the maximum number of hydrogen atoms per carbon atoms are called _____saturated_____ compounds.

3. Which family of hydrocarbons are always saturated compounds?

   _____alkanes_____

4. Circle the letter of the correct name for the alkene shown below.

$$CH_3 \diagdown \diagup CH_3$$
$$C = C$$
$$CH_3 \diagup \diagdown CH_2CH_3$$

   a. 2,3-dimethyl-3-pentene   (**c.**) 2,3-dimethyl-2-pentene

   b. 2-methyl-3-methyl-2-pentene   **d.** 3-ethyl-2-methyl-2-butene

5. Is the following sentence true or false? Rotation can occur around a carbon–carbon double bond. _____false_____

▶ **Alkynes (page 703)**

6. Hydrocarbons that contain one or more _____triple_____ covalent bonds between carbons are called alkynes.

7. _____Ethyne_____ is the simplest alkyne, and is also known by the common name _____acetylene_____ .

CHAPTER 22, Hydrocarbon Compounds *(continued)*

8. Circle the letter of each compound that is an aliphatic compound.

(**a.**) 1-butene

(**b.**) acetylene

(**c.**) 2-methylpropane

9. What are the major attractive forces between alkane, alkene, or alkyne molecules?

The major forces are weak van der Waals forces.

10. Complete the table below with the names of the indicated alkanes, alkenes, and alkynes. For the alkenes and alkynes, assume that the multiple bond occurs between the first two carbons.

Number of Carbons	Alkane	Alkene	Alkyne
C_6	hexane	1-hexene	1-hexyne
C_7	heptane	1-heptene	1-heptyne
C_8	octane	1-octene	1-octyne

11. Is the following sentence true or false? The angle between the carbon atoms in a carbon–carbon triple bond is 120°. _____false_____

SECTION 22.3 ISOMERS (pages 704–707)

This section explains how to distinguish among structural, geometric, and stereoisomers. It also describes how to identify the asymmetric carbon or carbons in stereoisomers.

▶ Structural Isomers (page 704)

1. What are structural isomers?

They are compounds that have the same molecular formula but the atoms are joined together in a different order.

2. Is the following sentence true or false? Structural isomers have the same physical properties. _____false_____

3. How many structural isomers are there for C_4H_{10}? _____two_____

4. Name the structural isomers of C_4H_{10}. _____butane and 2-methylpropane_____

5. In general, what determines which of two structural isomers will have the lower boiling point? In general, the more highly branched structure will have the lower boiling point.

▶ **Stereoisomers** (pages 705–706)

6. Stereoisomers differ only in the _____position of their atoms_____ .

7. What two things need to be present for geometric isomers to exist?

   a. a double bond _____

   b. at least one substituent on each carbon of the double bond _____

8. What are the names of the molecules represented by the ball-and-stick models below?

   _____*cis*-2-butene_____   _____*trans*-2-butene_____

9. Objects that are _____symmetrical_____ will produce a reflection that is indistinguishable from the original object.

10. Mirror images of a right hand and a left hand cannot be _____superimposed_____ .

11. What is an asymmetric carbon?

   It is a carbon with four different atoms or groups attached. _____

12. Is the following sentence true or false? The relationship of optical isomers is similar to that between right and left hands. _____true_____

13. Look at Figure 22.9 on page 705. Why are these two molecules optical isomers?

   They contain an asymmetric carbon atom. _____

   _____

14. Circle the two asymmetric carbons in the structure shown below.

   CH_3—CH_2—CH_2—ⒸH—ⒸH—CH—CH_3
                                  CH_2 CH_3 CH_3
                                  CH_3

CHAPTER 22, Hydrocarbon Compounds *(continued)*

SECTION 22.4 HYDROCARBON RINGS (pages 709–711)

This section describes how to identify and classify cyclic hydrocarbons. It also explains the bonding in benzene.

▶ **Cyclic Hydrocarbons** (page 709)

1. What is a cyclic hydrocarbon?

   It is a compound that contains a hydrocarbon ring. _____

2. The most abundant cyclic hydrocarbons contain _____ five _____ or _____ six _____ carbons.

3. What are the names of the cyclic hydrocarbons represented below?

   a. _cyclohexane_   **b.** _cyclopentane_   **c.** _cyclobutane_   **d.** _cyclopropane_

4. Is the following sentence true or false? Cyclic hydrocarbons that contain only single carbon–carbon bonds are called cycloalkanes. _____ true _____

▶ **Aromatic Hydrocarbons** (pages 710–711)

5. What is the origin of the name *aromatic compounds*?

   Many aromatic compounds have pleasant odors. _____

6. Benzene has the chemical formula _____ C_6H_6 _____ .

7. Is the following sentence true or false? Any substance that has carbon–carbon bonding like that of benzene is called an aromatic compound. _____ true _____

8. Another name for an aromatic compound is a(an) _____ arene _____ .

9. What does it mean to say that benzene exhibits resonance?

   Two equally valid structures can be drawn for benzene. _____

10. Molecules that exhibit resonance are more _____ stable _____ than similar molecules that do not exhibit resonance.

11. The actual bonds in a benzene ring are identical _____ hybrids _____ of single and double bonds.

12. When _____ benzene _____ is a substituent on an alkane, it is called a phenyl group.

13. Circle the letter of the name of the compound shown below.

    a. ethylhexene

    b. dimethylbenzene

    (**c.**) ethylbenzene

14. Derivatives of benzene that have _____two_____ substituents are called disubstituted benzenes.

15. Why do disubstituted benzenes always have three structural isomers?

There are three possible positions for the two substituents.

Match the terms for naming a disubstituted benzene with the substituent positions they represent.

   __b__ **16.** *meta*   **a.** 1,2

   __a__ **17.** *ortho*   **b.** 1,3

   __c__ **18.** *para*   **c.** 1,4

19. What is another name for the dimethylbenzenes? _____xylenes_____

SECTION 22.5 HYDROCARBONS FROM EARTH'S CRUST
(pages 712–715)

This section describes the origin, composition, and uses of natural gas, petroleum, and coal.

▶ Natural Gas (page 712)

1. What are fossil fuels?

They are carbon–based fuels derived from the decay of organisms.

2. List three factors needed to produce fossil fuels from organic residue.

   a. _____pressure_____

   b. _____bacterial action_____

   c. _____heat_____

3. Petroleum and natural gas contain mostly _____aliphatic_____ hydrocarbons.

4. What are the four main components of natural gas?

methane, ethane, propane, and butane

5. Which noble gas is found in natural gas? _____helium_____

CHAPTER 22, Hydrocarbon Compounds *(continued)*

6. Fill in the missing reactants and products in the equation for the combustion of methane.

$$CH_4(g) + 2 \underline{\quad O_2 \quad} (g) \longrightarrow \underline{\quad CO_2 \quad} (g) + 2 \underline{\quad H_2O \quad} (g) + heat$$

7. Propane and butane are sold in _____ liquid _____ form to be used as _____ heating _____ fuels.

8. _____ Complete _____ combustion of a hydrocarbon produces a blue flame; _____ incomplete _____ combustion produces a yellow flame.

9. What toxic gas is formed during incomplete combustion of a hydrocarbon? _____ carbon monoxide (CO) _____

▶ Petroleum (page 713)

10. The first oil well was drilled in _____ Pennsylvania _____ in the late 1850s.

11. Is the following sentence true or false? Petroleum is commercially useful without refining. _____ false _____

12. How is petroleum refined?

It is refined by fractional distillation. Compounds are collected according to

their boiling points.

13. Circle the letter of the distillation fraction that represents the highest percent of crude oil.

   a. natural gas

   b. gasoline

   c. kerosene

   d. lubricating oil

14. Using a catalyst and heat to break hydrocarbons down into smaller molecules is called _____ cracking _____ .

15. Complete the table below about four fractions obtained from crude oil. Indicate where each fraction will be collected from the fractionating column shown at the right.

Fraction	Composition of Carbon Chains	Where in Column?
Fuel oil	C_{15} to C_{18}	C
Gasoline	C_6 to C_{12}	A
Kerosene	C_{12} to C_{15}	B
Lubricating oil	C_{16} to C_{24}	D

Fractionating Column
Gasoline vapors
Condenser
Gas
A
B
C
D
Crude oil vapors from heater
Steam
Residue (wax, asphalt, tar)

▶ Coal (pages 714–715)

16. _____Peat_____ is the intermediate material that is the first stage in coal formation.

17. Name the three types of coal and the carbon content of each.

   a. _____lignite; about 50%_____

   b. _____bituminous; 70–80%_____

   c. _____anthracite; > 80%_____

18. Is the following sentence true or false? Coal mines in North America are usually at least a kilometer below Earth's surface. _____false_____

19. Coal consists primarily of _____aromatic_____ compounds of extremely high molar mass.

20. Aromatic compounds produce more _____soot_____ when burned than do _____aliphatic_____ fuels.

21. What major air pollutants are produced by burning coal that contains sulfur?

   _____SO_2 and SO_3_____

22. List four products that can be obtained by distilling coal.

   a. _____gas_____   c. _____coke_____

   b. _____coal tar_____   d. _____ammonia_____

23. Which of these products can be distilled further?

   _____coal tar_____

CHAPTER 22, Hydrocarbon Compounds *(continued)*

GUIDED PRACTICE PROBLEM

GUIDED PRACTICE PROBLEM 3 (page 699)

3. Name these compounds according to the IUPAC system.

a. $CH_2 - CH_2 - CH - CH_2 - CH_3$
　　|　　　　　|
　　CH_3　　　CH_2
　　　　　　　|
　　　　　　　CH_3

b. $CH_3 - CH_2 - CH - CH_3$
　　　　　　　|
　　　　　　　CH_3

Use the steps on pages 698–699 to name each compound.

Step 1. How long is the longest string of carbon atoms? What is the name of the parent hydrocarbon structure?

a. _____ 6; hexane _____ b. _____ 4; butane _____

Step 2. From which side will you number the carbon chain? Why?

a. It should be numbered from the right, because the substituent is closer to this end.

b. It should be numbered from the right, because the substituent is closer to this end.

Step 3. What are the names and positions of the substituents?

a. _____ 3-ethyl _____ b. _____ 2-methyl _____

Step 4. Explain why neither name will contain a prefix.

a. Each compound has only one substituent.

Step 5. Does the name contain any commas or hyphens?

a. The name contains one hyphen, after the number. It contains no commas.

b. The name contains one hyphen, after the number. It contains no commas.

Step 6. What is the complete name of each compound?

a. _____ 3-ethylhexane _____ b. _____ 2-methylbutane _____

EXTRA PRACTICE PROBLEM (similar to Practice Problem 18, page 706)

18. Circle the symmetric carbon, if there is one, in each of these structures.

a. $CH_3 - CH - CH - CH_3$
　　　　　|　　　|
　　　　CH_3　CH_3

b. $CH_3 - \boxed{CH} - CH_2 - CH_2$
　　　　　　|　　　　　|
　　　　　CH_2　　　CH_3
　　　　　　|
　　　　　CH_3

23 FUNCTIONAL GROUPS

SECTION 23.1 INTRODUCTION TO FUNCTIONAL GROUPS (pages 725–729)

This section defines a functional group and gives several examples. It also describes halocarbons and the substitution reactions they undergo.

▶ Functional Groups (pages 725–726)

1. Is the following sentence true or false? The saturated hydrocarbon skeletons of organic molecules are chemically reactive. _____false_____

2. What is a functional group? _It is a specific arrangement of atoms in an organic_ _compound that is capable of characteristic chemical reactions._

Use Table 23.1 on page 726 to answer Questions 3 and 4.

3. Name the functional group for each compound structure.

   a. R — O — R ___ether___   **b.** R — OH ___hydroxyl___   **c.** R — NH$_2$ ___amino___

4. Name two compound types that have a carbonyl group as a functional group.

   a. ___aldehyde___   **b.** ___ketone___

▶ Halogen Substituents (pages 726–728)

5. What are halocarbons? _Halocarbons are a class of organic compounds containing_ _covalently bonded fluorine, chlorine, bromine, or iodine._

6. Give the IUPAC and common names for the following halocarbons.

   a. CH$_3$ — CH$_2$ — CH$_2$ — Br ___bromopropane, propyl bromide___

   b.
   $$\text{H}\diagdown\diagup\text{I}$$
   $$\text{C}=\text{C}$$
   $$\text{H}\diagup\diagdown\text{H}$$
   ___iodoethene, vinyl iodide___

7. A halogen attached to a carbon of an aliphatic chain produces a halocarbon called a(n) ___alkyl halide___ .

Match the prefix used in naming alkyl groups with its description.

   a. *iso-*   **b.** *sec-*   **c.** *tert-*

___c___ 8. The carbon joining this alkyl group to another group is bonded to three other carbons.

___b___ 9. The carbon joining this alkyl group to another group is bonded to two other carbons.

___a___ 10. The carbon joining this alkyl group to another group is bonded to one other carbon.

CHAPTER 23, Functional Groups *(continued)*

11. What is an aryl halide? It is a halocarbon in which a halogen is attached to a carbon of an arene ring.

▶ Substitution Reactions (pages 728–729)

12. Why do reactions involving organic compounds often proceed more slowly than those involving inorganic molecules and ions?

These reactions commonly involve the breaking of relatively strong covalent bonds.

13. Is the following sentence true or false? The products of organic reactions are often a complex mixture of compounds. __true__

14. Organic reactions that involve the replacement of one atom or group of atoms with another atom or group of atoms are called __substitution__ reactions.

15. Label the compounds in this generalized equation. (*X* stands for a halogen.)

$$R-H \ + \ X_2 \ \longrightarrow \ R-X \ + \ HX$$

  alkane   halogen   halocarbon   hydrogen halide

16. Hydroxide ions can displace most halogens on carbon chains to produce a(n) __alcohol__ .

SECTION 23.2 ALCOHOLS AND ETHERS (pages 730–736)

This section describes the structures and naming of alcohols and ethers, as well as comparing their properties. It also defines and gives examples of addition reactions.

▶ Alcohols (pages 730–731)

1. What are alcohols?

They are a class of organic compounds with an —OH group.

2. The functional group in an alcohol is called a(n) __hydroxyl__ group.

Match each structural category of aliphatic alcohols with its description.

__b__ 3. primary alcohol   **a.** three R groups attached to C — OH

__c__ 4. secondary alcohol   **b.** one R group attached to C — OH

__a__ 5. tertiary alcohol   **c.** two R groups attached to C — OH

6. Circle the letter of the IUPAC ending used for an alcohol with two — OH substitutions.

    a. *-ol*   **b.** *-tetrol*   **c.** *-triol*   **(d.)** *-diol*

7. _____ Glycol _____ is the common name for alcohols with more than one —OH substituent.

8. Write the IUPAC name and the common name for each alcohol shown.

   a. CH₃ — CH₂ — OH   _____ ethanol; ethyl alcohol _____

   b. CH₃ — CH — CH₃   _____ 2-propanol; isopropyl alcohol _____
            |
            OH

   c. CH₂ — CH — CH₂   _____ 1,2,3-propanetriol; glycerol _____
      | | |
      OH   OH   OH

▶ Properties of Alcohols (pages 732–733)

9. Is the following sentence true or false? Alcohols cannot form intermolecular hydrogen bonds. _____ false _____

10. What are the two parts of an alcohol molecule?

    the carbon chain and the hydroxyl group

11. Why are alcohols with four or more carbons not soluble in water?

    As the number of carbon atoms increases, the nonpolarity of the carbon chain

    becomes more significant than the polarity of the hydroxyl group.

12. Name two uses for isopropyl alcohol.

    a. It is used as an antiseptic.

    b. It is used as a base for cosmetics.

13. Which alcohol is used in many antifreezes? _____ ethylene glycol _____

14. The action of yeast or bacteria on sugars to produce ethanol is called
    _____ fermentation _____ .

15. How is ethanol denatured?

    A denaturant, usually methyl alcohol, is added to make it toxic.

▶ Addition Reactions (pages 733–735)

16. Adding new functional groups at the double or triple bond of an alkene or alkyne is called a(n) _____ addition _____ reaction.

17. Is the following sentence true or false? Adding a hydrogen halide to an alkene results in a disubstituted halocarbon. _____ false _____

CHAPTER 23, Functional Groups *(continued)*

18. Look at the reaction between ethene and water:

H₂C=CH₂ + H—OH $\xrightarrow[100°C]{H^+}$

a. Draw the structure of the product.

$$\begin{array}{c} H \quad OH \\ | \quad\ | \\ H-C-C-H \\ | \quad\ | \\ H \quad H \end{array}$$

b. What type of compound is the product? __an alcohol__

c. What is this type of addition reaction called? __a hydration reaction__

d. What is the role of the hydrogen ions? __a catalyst__

19. What type of reaction is used to manufacture margarine from unsaturated vegetable oils? __hydrogenation reaction__

20. Which hydrocarbon resists addition reactions? __benzene__

► Ethers (pages 735–736)

21. An ether is a compound in which __oxygen__ is bonded to two carbon groups.

22. How are ethers named? __The alkyl groups attached to the oxygen are named in alphabetical order, followed by the word ether.__

23. Circle the letter of each symmetrical ether.

a. ethylmethyl ether   **c.** diphenyl ether

b. diethyl ether   **d.** methylphenyl ether

24. Is the following sentence true or false? Ethers have higher boiling points than alcohols of comparable molar mass. __false__

Reading Skill Practice

By looking carefully at photographs and diagrams in your textbook, you can better understand what you have read. Look carefully at Figure 23.8 on page 734. What important idea do these photographs communicate? Do your work on a separate sheet of paper.

The photographs show the addition reaction between bromine and an unsaturated organic compound. They also show how bromine can be used to identify unsaturated compounds.

SECTION 23.3 CARBONYL COMPOUNDS (pages 737–746)

This section explains how to distinguish among the carbonyl groups of aldehydes, ketones, carboxylic acids, and esters. It also describes the reactions of compounds that contain the carbonyl group.

▶ Aldehydes and Ketones (pages 737–740)

1. A ___carbonyl group___ consists of a carbon joined by a double bond to an oxygen atom.

2. What is the difference between an aldehyde and a ketone? __An aldehyde always has__ __at least one hydrogen joined to the carbonyl group; in a ketone, the carbonyl group is__ __joined to two other carbons.__

3. What ending is used in the IUPAC system to indicate an aldehyde? a ketone?
   __-al; -one__

4. Circle the letter of each statement that is true about aldehydes and ketones.

   (**a.**) In an aldehyde or ketone sample, the molecules cannot form intermolecular hydrogen bonds.

   b. The molecules in an aldehyde or ketone sample do not attract each other through polar–polar interactions.

   c. Most aldehydes and ketones are gases at room temperature.

   (**d.**) Aldehydes and ketones can form weak hydrogen bonds with water.

Match the aldehyde or ketone with its use.

_b_	**5.** methanal	**a.**	almond flavoring
_d_	**6.** propanone	**b.**	preservative
_a_	**7.** benzaldehyde	**c.**	oil of cinnamon
_c_	**8.** 3-phenyl-2-propenal	**d.**	solvent

9. Aromatic aldehydes are often used as ___flavoring___ agents.

▶ Carboxylic Acids (pages 740–741)

10. What is a carboxyl group?
    __It is a carbonyl group attached to a hydroxyl group.__

11. Is the following sentence true or false? Carboxylic acids are weak acids. ___true___

12. What ending is used under the IUPAC system to designate a carboxylic acid?
    ___-oic acid___

13. Carboxylic acids with three or more carbons in a straight chain are also known as ___fatty___ acids.

CHAPTER 23, Functional Groups (continued)

14. Complete the table about saturated aliphatic carboxylic acids.

IUPAC Name	Common Name	Carbon Atoms	Formula
Butanoic acid	Butyric acid	4	$CH_3(CH_2)_2COOH$
Octanoic acid	Caprylic acid	8	$CH_3(CH_2)_6COOH$
Ethanoic acid	Acetic acid	2	CH_3COOH
Octadecanoic acid	Stearic acid	18	$CH_3(CH_2)_{16}COOH$

15. What form do all aromatic carboxylic acids have at room temperature?

crystalline solids _____

▶ **Esters** (pages 742–743)

16. An ester is a derivative of a _____ carboxylic acid _____ that has an —OR substituted for the —OH.

17. Write the general formula for an ester. _____ RCOOR _____

18. What two products are formed when an ester is hydrolyzed in the presence of a strong acid or base?

Acid: an alcohol and a carboxylic acid. Base: an alcohol and a salt of the acid.

▶ **Oxidation–Reduction Reactions** (pages 743–745)

19. Are triple carbon–carbon bonds more or less oxidized than double and single carbon–carbon bonds? _____ more _____

20. What is a dehydrogenation reaction? It is a reaction in which hydrogen atoms are _____ lost as double and triple bonds form between carbons. _____

21. Circle the letter of the compound that is the final product of methane oxidation.

    a. methanol   **c.** methanal

    b. formic acid   **d.** carbon dioxide

22. Primary alcohols are oxidized to form _____ aldehydes _____, but secondary alcohols form _____ ketones _____ when oxidized.

23. Why are tertiary alcohols resistant to oxidation? They cannot be oxidized because _____ there is no hydrogen present on the carbon bearing the hydroxyl group. _____

24. Is the following sentence true or false? The oxidation of organic compounds is exothermic. _____true_____

25. What property of aldehydes do Fehling's test and Benedict's test take advantage of? What color is the precipitate that forms?

aldehydes are easily oxidized; red

SECTION 23.4 POLYMERIZATION (pages 747–752)

This section defines polymers and monomers. It also names and describes the uses of some important addition and condensation polymers.

▶ Addition Polymers (pages 747–749)

1. What are polymers? Polymers are large molecules formed by the covalent bonding of repeating smaller molecules.

2. Is the following sentence true or false? Polymers can only contain one type of monomer. _____false_____

3. Most polymerization reactions require a _____catalyst_____ .

4. Complete the table by naming each polymer.

Polymer	Structure
Polyethylene	$H + CH_2 - CH_2 \,)_x\, H$
Polypropylene	$\begin{array}{c} CH_3 \\ \mid \\ + CH_2 - CH \,)_x \end{array}$
Polyvinyl chloride	$\begin{array}{c} Cl \\ \mid \\ + CH_2 - CH \,)_x \end{array}$
Teflon™	$+ CF_2 - CF_2 \,)_x$

Match the polymer with its use.

____d____ **5.** polyethylene   **a.** foam coffee cups

____a____ **6.** polystyrene   **b.** rubber tubing

____c____ **7.** polytetrafluoroethene   **c.** nonstick cookware

____b____ **8.** polyisoprene   **d.** plastic wrap

____e____ **9.** polyvinyl chloride   **e.** plumbing pipes

CHAPTER 23, Functional Groups *(continued)*

▶ Condensation Polymers (pages 750–752)

10. How is a polyester formed? <u>Repeating units of dicarboxylic acids and dihydroxy</u>
<u>alcohols are joined by ester bonds.</u>

11. For condensation polymerization to occur, each monomer molecule must
have _____<u>two</u>_____ functional groups.

12. Name the two monomer molecules that are joined to form the polyester PET.
<u>terephthalic acid and ethylene glycol</u>

13. Garments made from PET fibers are _____<u>wrinkle</u>_____ resistant.

14. Is the following sentence true or false? The polymer produced by the
condensation of a carboxylic acid and an amine is called an amide. ____<u>true</u>____

15. What common group of synthetic materials is made up by polyamides?
_____<u>nylon</u>_____

16. _____<u>Proteins</u>_____ are an important group of naturally occurring
polyamides made from monomers called _____<u>amino acids</u>_____ .

Match each common polymer to its structural representation.

<u>d</u> **17.**

    a. Kevlar
    b. Nomex
    c. nylon
    d. PET

<u>c</u> **18.**

<u>b</u> **19.**

<u>a</u> **20.**

THE CHEMISTRY OF LIFE

24

SECTION 24.1 A STRATEGY FOR LIFE (pages 763–765)

This section describes the structure of a typical eukaryotic cell. It also explains the relationship between photosynthesis and all life on Earth.

▶ The Structure of Cells (pages 763–764)

1. What are the two major types of cell design?

   a. _____prokaryotic cells_____   **b.** _____eukaryotic cells_____

2. Which of the two cell types are found in humans?

   _____eukaryotic cells_____

3. Fill in the missing labels for structures in the drawing of a eukaryotic cell.

nucleus   endoplasmic reticulum

mitochondrion

lysosome

4. Is the following sentence true or false? Both cell types are surrounded by a cell membrane that acts as a selective barrier to the passage of chemicals into or out of the cell. _____true_____

5. Only eukaryotic cells contain membrane-enclosed _____organelles_____ in which specialized functions of the cell occur.

Match the organelle to its function.

___c___ **6.** mitochondrion   **a.** manufacture of proteins

___b___ **7.** nucleus   **b.** cell reproduction

___d___ **8.** lysosome   **c.** energy production

___a___ **9.** endoplasmic reticulum **d.** digestion

CHAPTER 24, The Chemistry of Life *(continued)*

▶ Energy and Carbon Cycle (pages 764–765)

10. What is the source of all energy for life on Earth? _____ sunlight _____

11. Circle the letter of the process by which organisms capture solar energy and use it to make food.

   a. oxidation   **b.** photosynthesis   **c.** digestion   **d.** respiration

12. How do plants use the energy they obtain from sunlight?

   They use it to reduce carbon dioxide to carbon compounds that contain C — H bonds.

13. Explain how animals obtain the energy they need.

   They eat plants or animals that feed on plants. Then they break down glucose to

   release the energy stored in its chemical bonds.

14. What are the products of the oxidation of glucose?

   carbon dioxide and water

15. Is the following sentence true or false? The destruction of forests and pollution of the oceans has no effect on the survival of animal life.

   _____ false _____

SECTION 24.2 CARBOHYDRATES (pages 766-768)

This section describes the important structural characteristics of monosaccharides, disaccharides, and polysaccharides. It also lists the sources and uses for a number of important carbohydrates.

▶ Monosaccharides (pages 766–767)

1. Carbohydrates are made from aldehydes and ketones that contain many
   _____ hydroxyl _____ groups.

2. Name the three elements present in carbohydrates.

   a. _____ carbon _____   **b.** _____ hydrogen _____   **c.** _____ oxygen _____

3. What is the general formula for a carbohydrate? _____ $C_n(H_2O)_n$ _____

4. What is another name for simple sugars? _____ monosaccharides _____

5. Circle the letter of each simple sugar.

   a. glucose   **b.** sucrose   **c.** fructose   **d.** starch

▶ Disaccharides and Polysaccharides (pages 767–768)

6. Sugars formed by linking two monosaccharides are called _____ disaccharides _____ .

7. What compound is lost in the reaction that links two monosaccharides?
_____ water

8. Is the following sentence true or false? Sucrose, or table sugar, is formed by the polymerization of two glucose molecules. _____ false _____

9. What are polysaccharides? _They are large molecules formed by the polymerization_ of many monosaccharide monomers.

10. Complete the following table about polysaccharides.

Polysaccharide	Source	Function
starch	plants	energy storage
glycogen	animals	energy storage
cellulose	plants	structural (cell walls)

SECTION 24.3 AMINO ACIDS AND THEIR POLYMERS
(pages 769–773)

This section explains how to write a general formula for an amino acid and describes the bonding between amino acids. It also describes the effect of enzymes on biochemical reactions.

▶ Amino Acids (pages 769–770)

1. What is an amino acid? How many amino acids are found in living organisms?
An amino acid is any compound that contains an amino group and a carboxylic acid group in the same molecule; twenty amino acids are common in nature.

2. What determines the physical and chemical properties of an amino acid?
Each amino acid has a different side-chain group.

Match the amino acid to its abbreviation.

___d___ **3.** Glutamine   **a.** Ile

___a___ **4.** Isoleucine   **b.** Trp

___e___ **5.** Methionine   **c.** Pro

___c___ **6.** Proline   **d.** Gln

___b___ **7.** Tryptophan   **e.** Met

CHAPTER 24, The Chemistry of Life *(continued)*

▶ Peptides (page 770)

8. What is a peptide?

   It is any combination of amino acids that are joined by the formation of a bond

   between the amino group of one acid and the carboxylic acid group of another.

9. The bond between amino acids is called a(n) _____peptide_____ bond.

10. Is the following sentence true or false? The bond between amino acids always

    involves the side chains. _____false_____

11. The formula for peptides is written so that the free _____amino_____

    group is on the left end and the free _____carboxylic acid_____ group is on the

    right end.

12. Is the following sentence true or false? The order of the amino acids in a

    peptide can be reversed and still represent the same peptide. _____false_____

▶ Proteins (pages 770–771)

13. A(n) _____polypeptide_____ contains more than ten amino acids, but a(n)

    _____protein_____ has more than 100 amino acids.

14. The chemical and physiological properties of a protein are determined by its

    _____amino acid_____ sequence.

15. Name each type of structure that can be formed by folding long peptide
    chains.

    _____helix_____   _____sheet_____

16. What types of bonds maintain the three-dimensional shape of a folded

    protein? _hydrogen bonds between adjacent parts of the folded chain and covalent_

    bonds between sulfur atoms in cysteine monomers

17. Is the following sentence true or false? A single protein can be made from

    separate polypeptide chains, held together by bonds between side-chain

    groups. _____true_____

▶ Enzymes (pages 772–773)

18. What are enzymes?

    They are proteins that act as catalysts in the chemical reactions of organisms.

19. What three properties of a catalyst do enzymes have?

a. They increase the reaction rate.

b. They are unchanged by the reaction.

c. They do not change the equilibrium position.

20. Is the following sentence true or false? Because an active site fits a specific substrate, each enzyme catalyzes only one chemical reaction.

_____ true _____

21. What is the enzyme molecule joined to its substrate molecule called?

enzyme-substrate complex

Match the enzyme to its substrate.

_____c_____ **22.** urease   **a.** carbonic acid

_____a_____ **23.** carbonic anhydrase   **b.** hydrogen peroxide

_____b_____ **24.** catalase   **c.** urea

25. What is a coenzyme? Give two examples. It is a nonprotein cofactor that assists an

enzyme in a chemical reaction. Two examples are water-soluble vitamins and metal ions.

SECTION 24.4 LIPIDS (pages 775–777)

This section characterizes the molecular structure of triglycerides, phospho-lipids, and waxes. It also describes the functions of phospholipids and proteins in cell membranes.

▶ Triglycerides (pages 775–776)

1. Fats provide an efficient means of _____ energy storage _____ for your body.

2. What are lipids? They are fats, oils, and other water-insoluble compounds.

3. Triglycerides are triesters of one _____ glycerol _____ molecule and three _____ fatty acid _____ molecules.

4. Complete the following table about two types of triglycerides.

Triglyceride Type	State at Room Temperature	Primary Source
fats	solid	animals
oils	liquid	plants

5. Circle the letter of the process used to make soap.

a. hydrogenation   **c.** denaturation

b. saponification   **d.** polymerization

CHAPTER 24, The Chemistry of Life *(continued)*

▶ Phospholipids (pages 776–777)

6. What is the molecular structure of a phospholipid?

It is a lipid that contains a phosphate group.

7. How does the chemical nature of a phospholipid affect its solubility?

It has an ionic head that is hydrophilic and soluble in water, and a hydrocarbon tail

that is hydrophobic and water-insoluble.

8. When phospholipids are added to water, they spontaneously form a lipid

_____ bilayer _____ , with the hydrophobic tails located in the

_____ middle _____ .

9. How does a cell membrane accomplish selective absorption?

The lipid bilayer acts as a barrier against the passage of material into or out of the

cell. Proteins in the lipid bilayer form channels that allow specific ions and molecules

to pass through them, while excluding others.

▶ Waxes (page 777)

10. What is the molecular structure of waxes?

They are esters of long-chain fatty acids and long-chain alcohols.

11. Is the following sentence true or false? Waxes are liquid at room temperature.

_____ false _____

12. Name two functions of waxes in plants.

protect plants from attacking microorganisms and prevent water loss

SECTION 24.5 NUCLEIC ACIDS (pages 778–785)

This section describes the structural components of nucleotides and nucleic acids, including DNA, and gives simple examples of genetic mutations. It also explains what is meant by recombinant DNA technology.

▶ DNA and RNA (pages 778–779)

1. What are the functions of the two types of nucleic acids?

DNA stores information to make proteins and it regulates cell growth and reproduction.

RNA transmits the stored information to the cells.

2. The monomers that make up nucleic acids are called _____ nucleotides _____ .

Name _____ Date _____ Class _____

3. Name the three parts of a nucleotide.

   a. _____phosphate group_____   **b.** _____five-carbon sugar_____   **c.** _____nitrogen base_____

4. What nitrogen bases are found in DNA? in RNA?

   DNA contains adenine, guanine, thymine, and cytosine. RNA contains uracil, instead

   of thymine, in addition to adenine, guanine, and cytosine.

5. DNA molecules consist of two chains of nucleotides that are bound together

   into a double _____helix_____ .

6. Name the complementary base pairs found in DNA.

   a. _____A and T_____   **b.** _____G and C_____

▶ The Genetic Code (pages 780–781)

7. What is a gene?

   It is the section of DNA that contains the information to make one type of protein.

8. How many nucleotides are needed to code for one amino acid? ____three____

9. The _____genetic code_____ is the arrangement of code words in DNA that
   provides the information to make specific proteins.

10. Is the following sentence true or false? Each amino acid has only one DNA
    code word. _____false_____

11. Use Table 24.2 on page 781. Which amino acids are coded in the nucleotide
    sequence TACAGCCTCGACAAG?

    Met, Ser, Glu, Leu, Phe

12. Circle the letter of each code word that represents a termination signal.

    (a.) ATT   **b.** AAC   **(c.)** ATC   **d.** AAT

▶ Gene Mutations (pages 782–783)

13. Circle the letter of each event that could cause a gene mutation.

    (a.) substitution of one or more nucleotides

    (b.) addition of one or more nucleotides

    (c.) deletion of one or more nucleotides

14. What is the effect of mutations on the production of proteins?

    Usually, a defective protein will be produced or no protein at all. Sometimes the

    protein produced is beneficial.

CHAPTER 24, The Chemistry of Life *(continued)*

15. Is the following sentence true or false? Diseases resulting from gene mutations are called inborn errors. _____ true _____

16. Name two diseases that are caused by mutations in the hemoglobin gene.

sickle cell anemia and methemoglobinemia

▶ DNA Fingerprinting (pages 783–784)

17. DNA base sequences differ for everyone except _____ identical twins _____ .

18. Complete the flowchart about DNA fingerprinting.

Obtain a small sample of DNA from _____ hair, body fluids, or skin cells _____ .

↓

_____ Amplify _____ the amount of DNA by millions of times.

↓

Use _____ enzymes _____ to cut the DNA into fragments.

↓

Separate and _____ visualize _____ the fragments.

↓

Compare the DNA fingerprint, or _____ pattern _____ , with a DNA sample from a known individual.

19. What are the disadvantages of DNA fingerprinting in criminal cases?

The sample cannot be identified as belonging to one individual with absolute certainty,

and the results are often subject to interpretation.

▶ Recombinant DNA Technology (pages 784–785)

20. Describe the three steps in the production of recombinant DNA.

a. cleaving a DNA chain

b. inserting a new piece of DNA into the gap

c. resealing the chain

21. Name three medicines that are produced by recombinant DNA technology.

a. _____ insulin _____ **b.** _____ tissue plasminogen activator _____ **c.** _____ interferon _____

22. What is a clone? It is an exact genetic copy of a single parent.

SECTION 24.6 METABOLISM (pages 786–790)

This section describes the role of ATP in energy production and energy use in the cell. It also defines metabolism and explains the relationship between catabolism and anabolism.

▶ **ATP** (pages 786–787)

1. What is ATP and what is its function?

   Adenosine triphosphate transmits energy needed by cells.

2. Energy is captured when a _____ phosphate _____ group is added to adenosine diphosphate (ADP).

3. **a.** How much energy is stored when one mole of ATP is produced? _____ 30.5 kJ

   b. How much energy is released when one mole of ATP is hydrolyzed back to ADP? _____ 30.5 kJ

4. ATP is important because it occupies an _____ intermediate _____ position between higher-energy _____ oxidation _____ reactions and other cellular processes.

▶ **Catabolism** (pages 787–788)

5. The entire set of all chemical reactions that are carried out in a living organism is called _____ metabolism _____ .

6. What is catabolism? It is the collection of reactions that degrade food and unneeded cellular components to simpler compounds.

7. Circle the letter of each product of catabolism.

   (a.) heat   c. complex biological molecules

   (b.) ATP   (d.) building blocks for new compounds

8. One of the most important catabolic processes is the complete oxidation of _____ glucose _____ to form _____ carbon dioxide _____ and water.

9. How much energy is released by the complete combustion of one mole of glucose? _____ 2.82×10^3 kJ

10. How many moles of ATP are produced by the complete oxidation of one mole of glucose? _____ up to 38 moles of ATP

11. Is the following sentence true or false? All the reactions involved in the complete oxidation of glucose are shown in Figure 24.25.

    _____ false

CHAPTER 24, The Chemistry of Life *(continued)*

12. Use Figure 24.25 to fill in the names of the carbon-containing molecules and ions represented.

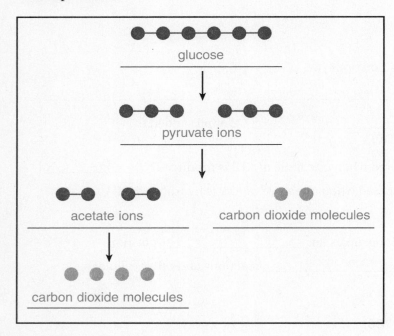

▶ Anabolism *(page 788)*

13. Anabolic reactions are _____*synthesis*_____ reactions that produce more-complex biological molecules.

14. Catabolic reactions _____*produce*_____ energy, whereas anabolic reactions _____*use*_____ energy.

15. Look at Figure 24.26. Explain why all the terms that appear in the yellow ovals also appear in the blue ovals.

    Complex biological molecules such as proteins are broken down during catabolism into

    intermediate carbon compounds, which can be used to build other complex biological

    molecules necessary for the health and growth of an organism.

▶ The Nitrogen Cycle *(pages 789–790)*

16. A family of plants called legumes reduces atmospheric nitrogen to ammonia in a process called _____*nitrogen fixation*_____.

17. Certain bacteria reduce atmospheric nitrogen into ammonia in a process called _____*nitrogen fixation*_____.

18. How do nitrogen fertilizers enter the biosphere?

They are taken up by plants.

 Reading Skill Practice

By looking carefully at photographs and drawings in your textbook, you can better understand what you have read. Look carefully at Figure 24.27 on page 789. What important ideas does this drawing communicate? Do your work on a separate sheet of paper.

In the nitrogen cycle, atmospheric nitrogen enters the biosphere by biological fixation, industrial fixation, and lightning. Plants and animals incorporate ammonia into nitrogen compounds such as proteins, nucleic acids, and ATP. Decaying plants and animals return nitrogen to the soil. Denitrifying bacteria then return nitrogen to the atmosphere.

25 NUCLEAR CHEMISTRY

SECTION 25.1 NUCLEAR RADIATION (pages 799–802)

This section describes the nature of radioactivity and the process of radioactive decay. It characterizes alpha, beta, and gamma radiation in terms of composition and penetrating power.

▶ Radioactivity (pages 799–800)

1. Which French chemist noticed that uranium salts could fog photographic plates, even without being exposed to sunlight?
   _____Antoine Henri Becquerel_____

2. What name did Marie Curie give to the process by which materials give off rays capable of fogging photographic plates? ____radioactivity____

3. An isotope that has an unstable nucleus is called a(n) ____radioisotope____ .

4. Complete the table below to show basic differences between chemical and nuclear reactions.

Type of Reaction	Is Nucleus of Atom Changed?	Is Reaction Affected by Temperature, Pressure, or Catalysts?
Chemical	no	yes
Nuclear	yes	no

5. Complete the flowchart below, which describes the radioactive decay process.

The presence of too many or too few ____neutrons____ relative to protons leads to an unstable nucleus.

↓

At some point in time, an unstable nucleus will undergo a reaction and lose energy by emitting ____radiation____ .

↓

During the process of radioactive decay, an ____unstable____ radioisotope of one element is transformed eventually into a ____stable____ isotope of a different element.

CHAPTER 25, Nuclear Chemistry *(continued)*

▶ Types of Radiation (pages 800–802)

6. Complete the following table showing some characteristics of the main types of radiation commonly emitted during radioactive decay.

Type	Alpha Particle	Beta Particle	Gamma Radiation
Consists of	2 protons and 2 neutrons	electron (or positron)	high-energy electromagnetic radiation
Mass (amu)	4	$\frac{1}{1837}$	0
Penetrating power (low, moderate, or high)	low	moderate	high
Minimum shielding	sheet of paper	metal foil	thick concrete or lead

7. Look at Figure 25.2a on page 801. It shows the alpha decay of uranium-238 to thorium-234.

   a. What is the change in atomic number after the alpha decay?

   It decreases by 2.

   b. What is the change in mass number after the alpha decay?

   It decreases by 4.

8. When are radioisotopes that emit alpha particles dangerous to soft tissues?

   These radioisotopes are dangerous when they are ingested.

9. Look at Figure 25.2b on page 801. This diagram shows the beta decay of carbon-14 to nitrogen-14.

   a. What is the change in atomic number after the beta decay?

   It increases by 1.

   b. Which quantity changes in beta decay, the mass number or the charge of the nucleus? the charge of the nucleus

10. Explain how gamma radiation is similar to visible light, and how it is different.

    Similar: Both are forms of electromagnetic radiation.

    Different: Gamma radiation has much higher energy than visible light.

11. When are gamma rays emitted? Gamma rays are often emitted along with alpha or beta particles by the nuclei of disintegrating atoms.

12. Is the following sentence true or false? Gamma rays have no mass and no electrical charge. _____ true _____

13. Look at the diagram below. Below each material indicate with a checkmark which type of radiation—alpha, beta, or gamma—can be stopped by each material.

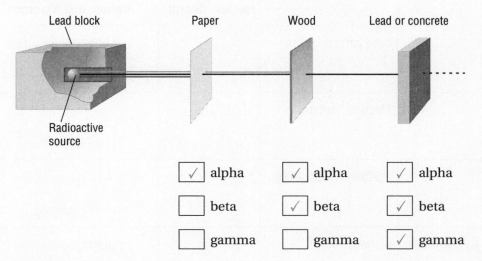

☑ alpha	☑ alpha	☑ alpha
☐ beta	☑ beta	☑ beta
☐ gamma	☐ gamma	☑ gamma

14. Is the following sentence true or false? X-rays are emitted during radioactive decay. _____ false _____

SECTION 25.2 NUCLEAR TRANSFORMATIONS (pages 803–808)

This section relates nuclear stability and decay to the ratio of neutrons to protons. It explains the use of half-life to measure the lifetime of unstable nuclei and gives examples of transmutations.

▶ Nuclear Stability and Decay (pages 803–804)

1. Of the more than 1500 different nuclei that are known to exist, about what portion are stable?

   a. 1 of 10   **(b.)** 1 of 6   **c.** 1 of 3   **d.** 1 of 2

2. For small atomic numbers, stable nuclei have roughly _____ equal _____ numbers of neutrons and protons.

3. Look at Figure 25.4 on page 803. How does the ratio of neutrons to protons for the stable nuclei change as atomic number increases from 1 to 82?

The ratio of neutrons to protons increases from 1 to about 1.5.

4. A positron has the mass of a(n) _____ electron _____ but its charge is _____ positive _____ .

CHAPTER 25, Nuclear Chemistry *(continued)*

5. Complete the table below showing changes in charge and number of neutrons and protons for different types of nuclear decay.

Reason Nucleus Is Unstable	Type of Decay	Change in Nuclear Charge	Change in Number of Protons and Neutrons
Too many neutrons	Beta particle	+1	p increases by 1 n decreases by 1
Too many protons	Electron capture	−1	p decreases by 1 n increases by 1
Too many protons	Positron (Beta particle)	−1	p decreases by 1 n increases by 1
Too many protons and neutrons	Alpha particle	−2	p decreases by 2 n decreases by 2

▶ Half-Life (pages 804–806)

6. What is half-life? _the time it takes for half of the nuclei in a radioactive sample to_
   decay

7. Look at Table 25.3 on page 805 to help you answer the following questions.

   a. What is the half-life in years of carbon-14? _5730 years (or 5.73×10^3 years)_

   b. How many years old is an artifact that contains 50% of its original carbon-14? An artifact that contains 25% of its original carbon-14?

   5730 years; 11,460 years

   c. What radiation is emitted when potassium-40 decays?

   Beta particles and gamma rays are emitted.

   d. What is the half-life of potassium-40? _1.25×10^9 years_

   e. Which isotopes listed in Table 25.3 have a half-life similar to that of potassium-40? _uranium-235 and uranium-238_

8. The decay reaction below shows how a radioactive form of potassium found in many minerals decays into argon (gas). Fill in the missing mass number and atomic number for the argon isotope that results from the decay of potassium-40.

$$^{40}_{19}\text{K} + \,^{0}_{-1}\text{e} \longrightarrow \boxed{^{40}_{18}}\text{Ar}$$

▶ Transmutation Reactions (pages 807–808)

9. The conversion of an atom of one element to an atom of another element is called ____transmutation____ .

10. What are two ways transmutation can occur? __It can occur by radioactive decay or__ __by bombardment of the nucleus of an atom with a high-energy particle.__

11. Uranium-238 undergoes 14 transmutations before it reaches the stable isotope ____lead-206____ .

12. Is the following sentence true or false? All transuranium elements were synthesized in nuclear reactors and accelerators. ____true____

Reading Skill Practice

By looking carefully at photographs and graphs in your textbook, you help yourself understand what you have read. Look carefully at Figure 25.5 on page 804. What important idea does this graph communicate? If you were to extend the curve indefinitely, would the percent of radio-isotope remaining ever cross 0%? Why or why not? Do your work on a separate sheet of paper.

The graph shows that for any radioactive element, after each period of time equal to the half-life, the percent of the original radioisotope remaining is cut in half. Because the percent remaining is always positive, half of that is always positive, so the curve would never cross 0%.

CHAPTER 25, Nuclear Chemistry *(continued)*

SECTION 25.3 FISSION AND FUSION OF ATOMIC NUCLEI (pages 810–813)

This section describes nuclear fission and nuclear fusion. It discusses their potential as sources of energy, methods used to control them, and issues involved in containment of nuclear waste.

▶ Nuclear Fission (pages 810–811)

1. When certain heavy isotopes are bombarded with _____neutrons_____, they split into smaller fragments.

2. Use the following labels to complete the diagram below: *fission, fission fragments,* and *neutrons/chain reaction.*

3. The uncontrolled fission of 1 kg of uranium-235 can release energy equal to _____20,000_____ tons of dynamite.

4. Look at Figure 25.11 on page 811. This figure shows the basic components of a nuclear power reactor.

   a. What part of the reactor contains the nuclear fuel?

   The fuel rods contain the nuclear fuel.

   b. What are the two parts of the reactor that control the fission reaction, one by reducing the speed of neutrons, the other by absorbing neutrons?

   These parts are the moderator and the control rods.

   c. What is the role of the coolant? The coolant removes heat from the reactor core.

   The heat is used to generate steam.

▶ Nuclear Waste (page 812)

5. Which parts of a nuclear reactor must be removed and replaced periodically?
fuel rods

6. Look at Figure 25.12 on page 812. Where are spent fuel rods stored in a typical nuclear power plant?
They are stored in racks at the bottom of a pool.

▶ Nuclear Fusion (page 813)

7. Look at Figure 25.13 on page 813. What happens to each pair of hydrogen nuclei during nuclear fusion?
They combine and produce two positions and a helium nucleus, with the release of energy.

8. What problem has prevented the practical use of nuclear fusion?
The temperatures required to start a fusion reaction make it difficult to contain and control.

SECTION 25.4 RADIATION IN YOUR LIFE (pages 816–819)

This section explains three methods of detecting radiation and describes applications of radioisotopes in medicine and research.

▶ Detecting Radiation (page 816–817)

1. Why are beta particles called ionizing radiation? They have enough energy to knock electrons off some atoms of the bombarded substance to produce ions.

2. A device that detects flashes of light after ionizing radiation strikes a specially coated phosphor surface is called a _____ scintillation counter _____ .

▶ Using Radiation (pages 818–819)

3. How is neutron activation analysis used?
It can be used to detect trace elements in a sample.

4. Look at Figure 25.15 on page 819. How is radioactive iodine-131 being used as a diagnostic tool? Doctors can diagnose thyroid conditions from scanned images because iodine-131 is absorbed by the thyroid gland.

CHAPTER 25, Nuclear Chemistry *(continued)*

GUIDED PRACTICE PROBLEMS

GUIDED PRACTICE PROBLEM 7 (page 806)

7. Manganese-56 is a beta emitter with a half-life of 2.6 h. What is the mass of manganese-56 in a 1.0-mg sample of the isotope at the end of 10.4 h?

Analyze

Step 1. What are the known values?

$(t_{1/2})$ = 2.6 h, initial mass = 1.0 mg, elapsed time = 10.4 h

Step 2. How many half-lives have passed during the elapsed time?

$$\text{Number of half-lives} = \frac{\text{elapsed time}}{t_{1/2}} = \frac{\boxed{10.4\ h}}{2.6\ h/\text{half-life}} = \boxed{4}\ \text{half-lives}$$

Solve

Step 3. Multiply the initial mass by $\frac{1}{2}$ for each half-life.

$$1.0\ \text{mg} \times \frac{\frac{1}{2} \times \frac{1}{2} \times \frac{1}{2} \times \frac{1}{2}}{} = \underline{\qquad 0.063 \qquad}\ \text{mg Mn-56}$$

Evaluate

Step 4. How do you know your answer is correct? The mass after four half-lives should be much lower than the original mass.

EXTRA PRACTICE (similar to Practice Problem 7, page 806)

7. Iodine-126 is a beta emitter with a half-life of 13 days. What is the mass of iodine-126 in a 8.0-mg sample of the isotope at the end of 39 days?

$$\frac{39\ \text{days}}{13\ \text{days/half-life}} = 3\ \text{half-lives};\ 8.0\ \text{mg} \times \frac{1}{2} \times \frac{1}{2} \times \frac{1}{2} = 1.0\ \text{mg}$$

GUIDED PRACTICE PROBLEM 8 (page 806)

8. A sample of thorium-234 has a half-life of 24.1 days. Will all the thorium undergo radioactive decay in 48.2 days? Explain.

Step 1. How many half-lives have passed in 50 days?

$$\frac{48.2\ \text{days}}{\boxed{24.1\ \text{days/half-life}}} = \boxed{2}\ \text{half-lives}$$

Step 2. What fraction of the thorium will remain after 50 days?

$$\frac{1}{2} \times \frac{1}{2} = \frac{1}{4}$$

Step 3. Will all the thorium decay in 50 days? Explain.

No; one-fourth of the original mass will remain.